Common Core
Georgia Performance Standards Practice
Workbook

Grade 4

Scott Foresman·Addison Wesley

enVisionMATH®
Common Core

Glenview, Illinois • Boston Massachusetts • Chandler, Arizona • Upper Saddle River, New Jersey

ISBN-13: 978-0-328-75114-3
ISBN-10: 0-328-75114-6

PEARSON

9 17

Contents

About This Guide

Pearson is pleased to offer to Georgia students this Common Core Georgia Performance Standards Practice Workbook. In it, you will find pages to help you become good math thinkers and problem-solvers. It contains these pages:

- Reteaching and Practice pages for each *enVisionMATH Common Core* lesson.

- Reteaching and Practice pages for each *enVisionMATH Common Core* Step-Up lesson.

- Common Core Georgia Performance Standards Practice pages. For each Common Core Georgia Performance Standard, you will find two pages of practice exercises.

- Practice for the PARCC Assessment. You will find a practice assessment, similar to the PARCC Assessment that you will be taking. The Practice End-of-Year Assessment has 45 items that are all aligned to the Common Core Georgia Performance Standards for Mathematical Content. The two Performance Tasks focus on the Standards for Mathematical Practice.

Meanings of Multiplication

There are 4 rows of 5.

Addition sentence:

$5 + 5 + 5 + 5 = 20$

Multiplication sentence:

$4 \times 5 = 20$

There are 3 boxes. There are 7 books in each box.

There are 3 groups of 7.

Addition sentence:

$7 + 7 + 7 = 21$

Multiplication sentence:

$3 \times 7 = 21$

Write an addition sentence and a multiplication sentence for each picture.

1.

_____

2.

_____

Write a multiplication sentence for each addition sentence.

3. $10 + 10 + 10 + 10 = 40$ _____

4. $3 + 3 + 3 + 3 + 3 + 3 = 18$ _____

5. Number Sense Explain how multiplication can help you find $7 + 7 + 7$.

_____

R 1·1

Name _____

Meanings of Multiplication

Write an addition sentence and a multiplication sentence for the picture.

1.

_____

_____

Write a multiplication sentence for each addition sentence.

2. 4 + 4 + 4 + 4 = 16   _____

3. 10 + 10 + 10 + 10 + 10 + 10 = 60   _____

4. Number Sense How could you use multiplication to find 7 + 7 + 7?

_____

5. A classroom desk has 4 legs. How many legs do
5 desks have altogether?   _____

6. Danielle planted 3 seeds in each of 6 different pots.
How many seeds did she plant?   _____

7. Which is the multiplication sentence for 2 + 2 + 2 + 2?

A 4 × 4 = 16

B 2 × 2 = 4

C 4 × 2 = 8

D 2 × 6 = 12

8. Writing to Explain Explain how you can use multiplication
to find 2 + 2 + 2 + 2.

_____

_____

Patterns for Facts

Pattern	Example
All multiples of two are even numbers.	2, 18, 44
All multiples of 5 end in 0 or 5.	25, 100, 220

For all multiples of nine, the sum of   27 $2 + 7 = 9$
the digits is always a multiple of 9.   63 $6 + 3 = 9$

1.   9
    $\times\ 5$

2.   2
    $\times\ 8$

3.   5
    $\times\ 8$

4.   9
    $\times\ 4$

5.   9
    $\times\ 3$

6.   2
    $\times\ 7$

7.   5
    $\times\ 3$

8.   5
    $\times\ 6$

9.   9
    $\times\ 2$

10.   5
    $\times\ 7$

11.   6
    $\times\ 3$

12.   2
    $\times\ 6$

13. How many baseball cards are in 4 packages?

_____

Item	Number in Package
Baseball cards	5
Stickers	2
Coupons	9

14. How many stickers do you get if you buy 9 packages?

_____

15. How many coupons do you get if you buy 7 packages?

_____

Patterns for Facts

1. 5
× 4
—

2. 2
× 3
—

3. 9
× 7
—

4. 5
× 2
—

5. 8
× 2
—

6. 5
× 3
—

7. 9
× 8
—

8. 9
× 4
—

9. $9 \times 6 =$ _____

10. $2 \times 7 =$ _____

11. $5 \times 5 =$ _____

Algebra Find the missing number.

12. _____ $\times 9 = 45$

13. $2 \times$ _____ $= 14$

14. A package of baseball cards includes 5 cards. How many baseball cards are in 5 packages?

_____

15. What is the value of the missing number?
$9 \times \boxed{} = 36$

A 6   **B** 4   **C** 3   **D** 2

16. Writing to Explain Milton needs to find the product of two numbers. One of the numbers is 9. The answer also needs to be 9. How will he solve this problem? Explain.

_____

_____

_____

Multiplication Properties

You can use the Properties of Multiplication to help you find products.

Commutative Property of Multiplication

You can multiply any two numbers in any order.

$2 \times 3 = 3 \times 2$

Identity Property of Multiplication

When you multiply any number by 1, the product is that number.

$7 \times 1 = 7$

Zero Property of Multiplication

When you multiply any number by 0, the product is also 0.

$3 \times 0 = 0$

---

1. $7 \times 3 = 3 \times$ _____ **2.** $4 \times 0 =$ _____

3. $5 \times 4 = 4 \times$ _____ **4.** $2 \times 1 =$ _____

5. $0 \times 7 =$ _____ **6.** $8 \times 3 = 3 \times$ _____

7. $9 \times 1 = 1 \times$ _____ **8.** $1 \times 5 =$ _____

9. Number Sense How do you know that $35 \times 5 = 5 \times 35$ without finding products?

_____

_____

_____

10. Writing to Explain Explain how you know that in $? \times 6{,}273 = 6{,}273$, the ? will be 1.

_____

Name _____

Multiplication Properties

1.
$$\begin{array}{r} 0 \\ \times\ 4 \\ \hline \end{array}$$

2.
$$\begin{array}{r} 1 \\ \times\ 3 \\ \hline \end{array}$$

3.
$$\begin{array}{r} 7 \\ \times\ 1 \\ \hline \end{array}$$

4.
$$\begin{array}{r} 5 \\ \times\ 0 \\ \hline \end{array}$$

5.
$$\begin{array}{r} 1 \\ \times\ 8 \\ \hline \end{array}$$

6.
$$\begin{array}{r} 3 \\ \times\ 0 \\ \hline \end{array}$$

7.
$$\begin{array}{r} 4 \\ \times\ 1 \\ \hline \end{array}$$

8.
$$\begin{array}{r} 6 \\ \times\ 0 \\ \hline \end{array}$$

9. $1 \times 1 =$ _____

10. $9 \times 0 =$ _____

11. $0 \times 0 =$ _____

Algebra Find the missing number. Tell which property can help you.

12. _____ $\times\ 3 = 0$

13. $1 \times$ _____ $= 4$

_____

_____

14. Ray has 4 boxes with 5 pens in each box. Kevin has 5 boxes with 4 pens in each. Who has more pens?

_____

15. Which property can help you find the missing number? _____ $\times\ 6 = 0$

_____

16. **Writing to Explain** Milton needs to find the product of two numbers. One of the numbers is 6. The answer also needs to be 6. How will you solve this problem? Explain.

_____

_____

_____

3, 4, 6, 7, and 8 as Factors

You can use breaking apart to help find the product.

Example How many baseball cards do you have if you have
4 packages with 6 cards in each package?

You need to find 4×6.

4 groups of 6 are the same as 4 groups of 3 plus 4 groups of 3.

$4 \times 3 = 12$

$4 \times 3 = 12$

$4 \times 6 = (4 \times 3) + (4 \times 3)$

$\qquad = 12 + 12$

$\qquad = 24$

You have 24 baseball cards.

Use breaking apart to find each product.

1. $3 \times 5 =$ _____

2. $9 \times 4 =$ _____

3. $6 \times 6 =$ _____

4. $3 \times 7 =$ _____

5. $5 \times 7 =$ _____

6. $8 \times 4 =$ _____

7. $6 \times 7 =$ _____

8. $7 \times 8 =$ _____

Compare. Use $<$, $>$, or $=$ to fill in each $\bigcirc$.

9. $7 \times 4 \bigcirc 7 \times 5$

10. $6 \times 6 \bigcirc 3 \times 7$

11. $8 \times 3 \bigcirc 3 \times 8$

12. $9 \times 5 \bigcirc 12 \times 3$

13. Number Sense Explain how 9×4 can help you find 9×8.

_____

_____

_____

3, 4, 6, 7, and 8 as Factors

For **1** through **8**, fill in each ____ .

1. $3 \times 10 = (2 \times 10) + (1 \times$ ___$)$

2. $2 \times$___$= (2 \times 5) + (2 \times 1)$

3. $4 \times 7 = (4 \times$___$) + (4 \times 2)$

4. $11 \times 8 = (11 \times 5) + (11 \times$ ___$)$

5. $3 \times 6 = (3 \times 1) + (3 \times$ ___$)$

6. $6 \times 6 = (6 \times$ ___$) + (6 \times 4)$

7. $7 \times$ ___ $= (7 \times 4) + (7 \times 3)$

8. $1 \times 8 = (1 \times$ ___$) + (1 \times 3)$

For **9** through **20**, use breaking apart to find each product.

9. 5×5 ____

10. 3×6 ____

11. 4×2 ____

12. 7×3 ____

13. 7×2 ____

14. 6×6 ____

15. 7×7 ____

16. 6×7 ____

17. 8×3 ____

18. 10×6 ____

19. 6×12 ____

20. 4×6 ____

For **21** through **29**, compare using $<$, $>$, or $=$ to fill in each $\bigcirc$.

21. $3 \times 4 \bigcirc 6 \times 1$

22. $5 \times 8 \bigcirc 6 \times 7$

23. $3 \times 6 \bigcirc 9 \times 2$

24. $8 \times 4 \bigcirc 7 \times 4$

25. $7 \times 5 \bigcirc 12 \times 3$

26. $5 \times 6 \bigcirc 3 \times 10$

27. $1 \times 8 \bigcirc 2 \times 3$

28. $4 \times 5 \bigcirc 2 \times 10$

29. $8 \times 6 \bigcirc 7 \times 7$

30. Candice has placed her seashells into 4 rows with 5 seashells in each row. How many seashells does she have? ____

31. A chessboard has 8 rows and 8 columns. Each row has 4 white squares and 4 black squares. Which expression below would give you the number of black squares on a chessboard?

    A 8×8 **B** 8×4 **C** 4×4 **D** $8 + 8$

32. **Writing to Explain** Using the breaking apart method, what is the best way to multiply 8 by 7?

_____

Problem Solving: Look for a Pattern

What pattern do you see?

1 A 2 B 3 C 4 D 5 E 6 F

The numbers alternate with letters of the alphabet, in order.
The pattern would continue like this:

7 G 8 H 9 I

What pattern do you see?

A	B	C
1	1	1
2	2	4
3	3	9
4	4	16
5		25

The number in column A is multiplied by the number in column B.
Column C is the product.

The last number in column B would be 5.

Look for a pattern. Draw the next two shapes.

1.

Look for a pattern. Write the three missing numbers.

2. 2, 4, 6, 8, _____ , _____ , _____

3. 2, 7, 12, 17, _____ , _____ , _____

4. 60, 52, 44, 36, _____ , _____ , _____

5. 88, 77, 66, 55, _____ , _____ , _____

Name _____

Problem Solving: Look for a Pattern

Look for a pattern. Draw the next two shapes.

1.

2.

Look for a pattern. Write the missing numbers.

3. 5, 8, 11, 14, 17, _____ , _____

4. 4, 6, 10, 16, 24, _____ , _____

Look for a pattern. Complete each number sentence.

5. 80 + 8 = 88

800 + 88 = 888

8,000 + 888 = _____

80,000 + 8,888 = _____

6. 10 + 1 = 11

100 + 1 = 101

1,000 + 1 = _____

10,000 + 1 = _____

Look for a pattern. Write the missing numbers.

7. Sally went to purchase tiles for her kitchen floor. She measured the floor to find how many tiles she needed to cover the floor. Sally decided to make a pattern. She chose 10 red tiles,

20 beige tiles, 30 white tiles, _____ black tiles, and _____ gray tiles to complete a pattern for the kitchen floor.

8. Reasoning Fill in the missing amounts to update Carl's savings passbook.

Carl's Savings Account		
Date	Deposit	Balance
4/7	$25	$945
4/14		$995
4/21	$25	
4/30	$50	
5/7		$1,095

Meanings of Division

When you divide, you separate things into equal groups.

Doris is making 8 box lunches, each with the same number of strawberries. She has a total of 32 strawberries. How many strawberries should go in each lunch?

What you think: Doris will have to place an equal number of strawberries in each box. She must put 32 strawberries into 8 equal groups. How many strawberries are in each group?

What you show: 8 equal groups

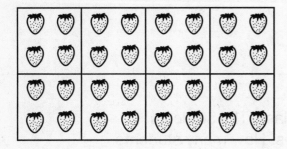

32 strawberries divided into 8 separate groups leaves 4 strawberries in each group.

What you write: 32 ÷ 8 = 4

32 is the dividend, the number that is being divided.

8 is the divisor, the number the dividend is being divided by.

4 is the quotient, or the answer to the division problem.

Each lunch should have 4 strawberries.

Draw pictures to solve each problem.

1. You put 15 marbles into 3 groups.
   How many marbles are in each group?

   _____

2. You need to put 20 ice cubes into
   5 glasses. How many cubes
   should go into each glass?

   _____

Meanings of Division

Draw pictures to solve each problem.

1. There are 12 small gift bags. Each bag can hold 1 toy and some stickers. There are 36 stickers. If an equal number of stickers is put in each bag, how many stickers will be in each bag?

_____

2. One egg carton holds 12 eggs. How many cartons are you able to fill with 60 eggs?

_____

3. There are 21 students in Mr. Tentler's class. The students divided themselves evenly into 3 groups. How many students are in each group?

_____

4. Calvin read an 18-page chapter in his social studies book in 2 hours. If he read the same number of pages each hour, how many pages did he read per hour?

   A 3 pages   **B** 6 pages   **C** 9 pages   **D** 12 pages

5. **Writing to Explain** A class is planning a party. A pizza restaurant cuts each pizza into 8 slices. There are 32 students. How many pizzas does the class need to order for each student to have a slice? Explain.

_____

_____

_____

Name _____

Relating Multiplication and Division

Multiplication and division are related, just like addition and subtraction are related.

This is the fact family for 5, 6, and 30:

$5 \times 6 = 30$ $30 \div 6 = 5$

$6 \times 5 = 30$ $30 \div 5 = 6$

Complete each fact family.

1. $2 \times$ _____ $= 10$

_____ $\times$ _____ $= 10$

$10 \div 5 =$ _____

$10 \div$ _____ $=$ _____

2. $9 \times$ _____ $= 27$

_____ $\times$ _____ $= 27$

$27 \div 3 =$ _____

$27 \div$ _____ $=$ _____

3. $8 \times$ _____ $= 72$

_____ $\times$ _____ $= 72$

$72 \div 8 =$ _____

$72 \div$ _____ $=$ _____

4. $6 \times$ _____ $= 48$

_____ $\times$ _____ $= 48$

$48 \div 8 =$ _____

$48 \div$ _____ $=$ _____

Write a fact family for each set of numbers.

5. 7, 4, 28

_____

6. 5, 8, 40

_____

7. Number Sense What multiplication facts are part of the fact family for $12 \div 3 = 4$?

_____

R 1·7

Relating Multiplication and Division

Complete each fact family.

1. $7 \times$ _____ $= 42$

_____ $\times$ _____ $= 42$

$42 \div 6 =$ _____

$42 \div$ _____ $=$ _____

2. $9 \times$ _____ $= 36$

_____ $\times$ _____ $= 36$

$36 \div 4 =$ _____

$36 \div$ _____ $=$ _____

Write a fact family for each set of numbers.

3. 6, 3, 18

_____

4. 5, 5, 25

_____

5. Reasoning Why does the fact family for 81 and 9 have only two number sentences?

_____

_____

_____

6. Which number sentence completes the fact family?

$9 \times 6 = 54$ $54 \div 9 = 6$ $54 \div 6 = 9$

A $9 \times 9 = 81$ **B** $6 \times 9 = 54$ **C** $6 \times 6 = 36$ **D** $8 \times 6 = 48$

7. Writing to Explain Find two ways to divide 16 evenly. Explain.

_____

_____

Special Quotients

There are special rules for dividing numbers by 1 and by 0.

Rule: A number divided by 1 is that number.

 Examples: $4 \div 1 = 4$ $55 \div 1 = 55$

Rule: A number divided by itself (except 0) is 1.

 Examples: $17 \div 17 = 1$ $135 \div 135 = 1$

Rule: Zero divided by a number (except 0) is 0.

 Examples: $0 \div 4 = 0$ $0 \div 15 = 0$

Rule: You cannot divide a number by zero.

 Examples: $7 \div 0$ cannot be done $12 \div 0$ cannot be done

1. $0 \div 2 =$ _____ **2.** $4 \div 4 =$ _____

3. $0 \div 7 =$ _____ **4.** $9 \div 9 =$ _____

5. $0 \div 3 =$ _____ **6.** $10 \div 10 =$ _____

7. $0 \div 11 =$ _____ **8.** $11 \div 1 =$ _____

Compare. Use >, <, or = for each ◯.

9. $6 \div 6 \bigcirc 3 \div 3$ **10.** $7 \div 1 \bigcirc 8 \div 8$

11. $0 \div 5 \bigcirc 3 \div 1$ **12.** $0 \div 4 \bigcirc 0 \div 9$

13. $5 \div 5 \bigcirc 0 \div 5$ **14.** $7 \div 7 \bigcirc 9 \div 9$

15. $8 \div 1 \bigcirc 0 \div 8$ **16.** $9 \div 9 \bigcirc 9 \div 1$

17. $0 \div 12 \bigcirc 12 \div 1$ **18.** $0 \div 11 \bigcirc 0 \div 15$

19. **Number Sense** If $a \div 4 = 0$, what do you
 know about a? _____

Name _____

Special Quotients

1. $0 \div 10 =$ _____   **2.** $7 \div 1 =$ _____   **3.** $8 \div 8 =$ _____

4. $9 \div 9 =$ _____   **5.** $0 \div 5 =$ _____   **6.** $5 \div 1 =$ _____

7. $1\overline{)4}$ _____   **8.** $8\overline{)0}$ _____   **9.** $3\overline{)3}$ _____   **10.** $1\overline{)6}$ _____

11. **Number Sense** If $x \div 9 = 1$, how do you know what x is? Explain.

_____

_____

12. Kenneth has 22 math problems to do for homework. He has 12 problems done. How many more problems does he have left? If he completes 1 problem every minute, how many more minutes does he have to work?

_____

13. There are 8 people who would like to share a box of granola bars that contains 8 bars. How many granola bars does each person get if they share equally?

_____

14. Which is the quotient of $20 \div 20$?

A 20   **B** 2   **C** 1   **D** 0

15. **Writing to Explain** Write the rule that applies to the following number sentence: $0 \div 7 = 0$.

_____

_____

_____

_____

Using Multiplication Facts to Find Division Facts

Tile Floor Darren is laying a tile floor in the hallway. The pattern for the floor is shown to the right.

First, use Darren's tile floor to write a multiplication story for
$4 \times 8 = 32$.

Darren's tile floor has 4 rows with 8 pieces of tile in each row. How many pieces of tile are there in all?

Second, use Darren's tile floor to write a division story for $32 \div 4 = 8$.

Darren has 32 small triangles. He needs 4 for each shaded square. How many shaded squares can he make with the small triangles?

Use the data in the table to write a multiplication or a division story for each number fact. Solve.

Building Supplies	Number in a Box
Fasteners	6
Bolts	12

1. 6×4

_____

_____

_____

2. $12 \div 4$

_____

_____

_____

Using Multiplication Facts to Find Division Facts

Solve.

1. 12 ÷ 3 = _____

2. 20 ÷ 5 = _____

3. 50 ÷ 10 = _____

4. 27 ÷ 9 = _____

5. 6 ÷ 2 = _____

6. 16 ÷ 8 = _____

7. 63 ÷ 9 = _____

8. 36 ÷ 4 = _____

9. 48 ÷ 6 = _____

10. 32 ÷ 8 = _____

11. 25 ÷ 5 = _____

12. 18 ÷ 2 = _____

Use the data in the table to write a multiplication story for the number fact. Solve.

13. 2 × 6 =

First Aid Kit	
Supply	**Number in Kit**
Bandages	4
Cleanser Pads	6
Cotton Balls	12

_____

_____

_____

14. Which is the quotient of 28 ÷ 7?

A 14   **B** 9   **C** 6   **D** 4

15. Writing to Explain Write a division story for 12 and 3.

_____

_____

_____

Problem Solving: Draw a Picture and Write an Equation

Draw a picture and write an equation.

Step 1:	**Step 2:**	**Step 3:**
Read and Understand	Plan and Solve	Look Back and Check

Step 1:
Read and Understand

Janie is in the fourth row of the marching band. There are 7 rows of musicians with 8 in each row. How many musicians are ahead of Janie? How many musicians are behind Janie?

You need to find how many are ahead of Janie and behind Janie.

Step 2:
Plan and Solve

You can draw a picture of the musicians: Write an A for each musician ahead of Janie, a B for each musician behind Janie, and a J for each musician in Janie's row.

Solve

```
A A A A A A A A ⎫
A A A A A A A A ⎬ 24
A A A A A A A A ⎭
J J J J J J J J  } 8
B B B B B B B B ⎫
B B B B B B B B ⎬ 24
B B B B B B B B ⎭
```

Step 3:
Look Back and Check

How many musicians are there ahead of Janie?
You can multiply.
$3 \times 8 = 24$

There are 24 musicians ahead of Janie.

How many musicians are behind Janie?
You can multiply.
$3 \times 8 = 24$

There are 24 musicians behind Janie.

---

1. James has 12 seashells mounted in a row. The 6 shells in the center of the row are nautilus shells. Is there the same number of shells on either side of the nautilus shells? Draw a picture to help you solve the problem.

_____

_____

Problem Solving: Draw a Picture and Write an Equation

For **1** through **4**, write an equation and solve. Use the picture to help.

1. John is running in a race. The race is 25 miles long. After two hours, John has run 7 miles. How many miles does John have left to run?

25 miles	
7	? miles

2. A summer camp has divided its campers into 8 groups of 9 campers. How many campers are at the summer camp?

? campers

| 9 | 9 | 9 | 9 | 9 | 9 | 9 | 9 |

3. Karen is 5 feet tall. In Karen's backyard there is an oak tree 4 times as tall as she is. How tall is the oak tree?

	? feet			
Oak tree	5ft	5ft	5ft	5ft
Karen	5ft			

4. Micah's room has four sides and a perimeter of 48 feet. If 3 of the sides are 12 feet long, how long is the fourth side?

48 feet			
12 ft	12 ft	12 ft	?

5. On Monday, Chris had $250 in his savings account. On Friday, he spent $16 at the movies. On Saturday, he deposited a $120 check. Which number sentence below shows how much money Chris has?

A 250 + 16 + 120

B 250 + 16 − 120

C 250 − 16 − 120

D 250 − 16 + 120

6. Melissa is making bookmarks from a piece of ribbon that is 12 inches long. Each bookmark is 4 inches long. She drew this picture to see how many bookmarks she could make from the ribbon. What did she do wrong?

12 inches in all			
4 inches	4 inches	4 inches	4 inches

Name _____

Repeating Patterns

Patterns can grow or patterns can repeat.
Repeating patterns can use numbers or shapes.
You can extend a pattern by finding a rule for the pattern.

Repeating Patterns with Shapes

Use this pattern.
What is the next shape?

Assign each shape a number. When a shape repeats use the same number.

The next shape is the second shape.

○

Repeating Patterns with Numbers

Use the pattern below. What is the 12th number in this pattern?

4, 7, 3, 5, 4, 7, 3, 5, 4, 7, ...

Find the pattern.
The pattern is 4, 7, 3, 5, and then it repeats.

Extend the pattern until reaching the 12th number.

4, 7, 3, 5, 4, 7, 3, 5, 4, 7, 3, 5

The 12th number is 5.

---

1. Draw the next three shapes in the pattern.

_____

2. What are the next three numbers in the pattern below?
5, 8, 3, 1, 5, 8, 3, 1, 5, 8

_____

3. **Explain It** In the pattern in Exercise 2, how could you find the 15th number? What is that number?

_____

_____

_____

Name _____

Repeating Patterns

Draw the next three shapes to continue the pattern.

1.

2.

_____   _____

Write the next three numbers to continue the pattern.

3. 4, 6, 2, 8, 4, 6, 2, 8, 4, …

4. 3, 3, 5, 3, 3, 5, 3, 3, 5, …

_____   _____

5. Draw a Picture What is the 12th shape in the pattern below?

6. Strategy Practice Penny has made a pattern of shapes on her bedroom walls. She drew a rectangle, 2 circles, a rectangle, and then 2 more circles until she drew 24 circles. How many shapes did she draw in all?

_____   _____

7. Mrs. Washington placed students in a line. The order was 1 boy, 2 girls, 2 boys, and continued. Was the 10th student a boy or a girl?

_____

8. What is the 15th number in the pattern below?
3, 6, 5, 2, 3, 6, 5, 2, …

A 2   **B** 3   **C** 5   **D** 6

Number Sequences

A number sequence is a pattern that increases or decreases while following a rule.

What are the next three numbers in this pattern?

36, 42, 48, 54, …

Step 1	**Step 2**
Find the pattern.	Use this rule to extend the pattern.
You can subtract to find the pattern.	Start with 54. Add 6.
$54 - 48 = 6$	$54 + 6 = 60$
$48 - 42 = 6$	$60 + 6 = 66$
$42 - 36 = 6$	$66 + 6 = 72$
Each number is 6 more than the number before it. So, a rule for the pattern is "add 6."	So, the next three numbers are 60, 66, and 72.

Find the next three numbers in each pattern.
Write a rule for the pattern.

1. 35, 40, 45, ■, ■, ■   2. 43, 39, 35, ■, ■, ■   3. 32, 39, 46, ■, ■, ■

_____   _____   _____

4. 13, 21, 29, ■, ■, ■   5. 75, 65, 55, ■, ■, ■   6. 51, 45, 39, ■, ■, ■

_____   _____   _____

7. **Critical Thinking** How can you use subtraction to complete an addition pattern? Use Exercise 3 as an example.

_____

_____

_____

Number Sequences

Find the missing numbers in each pattern. Write a rule for the pattern.

1. 19, 23, 27, ■, ■

2. 32, 26, 20, ■, ■

3. 125, 150, 175, ■, ■

_____ _____ _____

4. 8, 15, ■, ■, 36

5. 90, 80 ■, ■, 50

6. 84, 69, 54, ■, ■

_____ _____ _____

7. 30, 50, ■, 90, ■

8. 65, 56, ■, 38, ■

9. 35, ■, 57, 68, ■

_____ _____ _____

10. Reasoning The house numbers on Carr Memorial Avenue follow a pattern. The first four houses on the left side of the street are numbered 8, 14, 20, and 26. How many more houses are on the left side of the street with numbers less than 50?

_____

11. Noreen is beginning an exercise program. The first week she exercises 25 minutes each day. The second week she exercises 30 minutes a day and the third week she increases it to 35 minutes a day. If the pattern continues, how long will she exercise each day in the fifth week?

_____

12. Explain It What do you need to do to extend a number pattern?

_____

_____

_____

13. John said that 52 is part of the pattern below.
Mary said that 66 is part of the pattern below.
Who is correct?
18, 26, 34, 42, …

A Neither is correct.

B Both are correct.

C Only John is correct.

D Only Mary is correct.

Extending Tables

A table is an organized way to show a pattern.

Weeks	Days
1	7
3	21
5	35
6	42
8	?

Each pair of values follows some rule. If you can find a rule that works for all the pairs, you can extend the table.

What is the missing number in this table?

Step 1	**Step 2**
Find a rule for the pattern.	Use your rule to find the missing number.
The first 4 weeks are shown. You can divide to find the pattern.	Multiply the days in 1 week by the number of weeks.
$42 \div 6 = 7$ $35 \div 5 = 7$ $21 \div 3 = 7$ $7 \div 1 = 7$	$8 \times 7 = 56$
There are 7 days in one week.	The missing number is 56.

Complete each table.

1.

Cars	Wheels
1	4
2	8
3	
4	16
8	32

2.

Old Price	New Price
$63	$53
$48	$38
	$31
$37	$27
$26	$16

3.

Weight of Salad in Ounces	6	10	14	18
Total Weight of Container in Ounces	9	13	17	

Name _____

Extending Tables

Find the missing numbers.

1.

Number of Cats	Number of Legs
1	4
2	
3	12
4	16
	32

2.

Money Earned	Money Saved
$25	$15
$32	$22
$43	
	$47
$73	$63

3.

Touchdowns	Points
1	6
2	12
3	
	36
8	48

For **4** and **5**, use the table at the right.

T-shirts	Cost
1	$8
3	$24
5	$40

4. How much money would 9 T-shirts cost?

_____

5. Strategy Practice How much more money do 10 T-shirts cost than 6 T-shirts? Explain how you found your answer.

_____

_____

_____

6. Number Sense Bob has 3 bookshelves that hold a total of 27 books. He adds a fourth shelf and now has 36 books. If he adds 2 more shelves, how many books can he have in total?

_____

7. What is the missing number in the table below?

In	3	5	8	15
Out	9	11	14	

A 21   **B** 25   **C** 30   **D** 45

Name _____

Writing Rules for Situations

When working with tables, it is important to find a rule that works for all pairs of numbers. The rule tells how to find one of the numbers in a pair.

Old Price	New Price
$15	$10
$22	$17
$28	$23
$37	$32
$51	$46

Each pair of numbers in the table to the left follows a rule. If you can find a rule that works, you can extend the table.

Step 1

Find the pattern. Check the first pair of numbers to see how the first number changed to become the second number.

$15 - 10 = 5$

A rule for the first pair of numbers is "subtract 5."

Step 2

See if this rule works for all the values.

$22 - 17 = 5$	$37 - 32 = 5$
$28 - 23 = 5$	$51 - 46 = 5$

The rule "subtract 5" works for every pair of values.

Find the missing numbers in each table.
Write a rule for the table.

1.

Earned	Spent
$21	$14
$30	$23
$42	
$48	$41
$59	

2.

Teams	Players
3	27
8	72
6	
9	
2	18

3.

Tickets	Cost
2	$1
6	$3
12	
10	$5
20	

_____ _____ _____

4. Number Sense Joe said that by using the information in Exercise 2 there would be 250 players if there were 25 teams. Is that correct? Explain.

_____

_____

R 2·4

Writing Rules for Situations

Find the missing numbers in each table.
Write a rule for the table.

1.

Max's Age	Carol's Age
7	13
10	
14	20
18	24
	31

2.

Tricycles	Wheels
5	15
3	9
7	
	27
2	6

3.

Old Price	New Price
$25	$18
$16	$9
	$32
$53	$46
$72	

_____ _____ _____

For **4** and **5**, use the table at the right.

4. The table shows the number of players on a volleyball team. What is a rule for the table?

Players	Teams
24	4
48	8
36	6
30	5

_____

5. Explain It If there are 12 teams, how many players will there be? Explain how you found your answer.

_____

_____

6. How many miles can Nick travel in 5 hours? 6 hours?

Hours	1	2	3	4
Miles	60	120	180	240

_____

7. The table shows how many CDs Jim and Ken each own after joining a CD club. Which is a rule that works for this table?

Jim	8	12	20	30
Ken	16	20	28	38

A Add 8   **C** Subtract 10

B Multiply by 2   **D** Divide by 2

Name _____

Geometric Patterns

Like number patterns, geometric patterns can have figures that grow. To extend geometric patterns follow the same steps as you would for number patterns.

Below is a pattern of squares.

Number of Figure	1	2	3	4	5
Number of Squares	2	4	6		

Step 1	**Step 2**	**Step 3**
Look at the pattern. See how the figure has changed.	Make the next two figures.	Fill in the table.

Each figure grows by 1 square in height and 1 square in width.

Each figure grows by 2 squares.

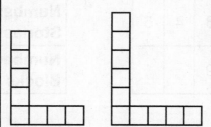

Fill in the table.

Number of Figure	1	2	3	4	5
Number of Squares	2	4	6	8	10

Draw the next two towers in the pattern. Use grid paper.
Find the missing numbers in each table.

1.

Number of Stories	1	2	3	4	5
Number of Blocks	4	8	12		

2.

Length of Sides	1	2	3	4	5
Sum of All Sides	5	10	15		

1   2   3

3. Number Sense If there were 10 stories in Exercise 1, how many blocks would there be? Explain.

_____

Geometric Patterns

Draw the next two figures in the pattern.
Find the missing numbers in each table.

1.

Number of Stories	1	2	3	4	5
Number of Blocks	5	10	15		

2.

Number of Stories	1	2	3	4	5
Number of Blocks	2	4	6		

3.

Length of Each Side	1	2	3	4	5
Sum of All Sides	3	6	9		

4.

Number of Stories	1	2	3	4	5
Number of Blocks	6	12	18		

5. Explain It Use Exercise 4. How could you find how many blocks there were in 20 stories? How many blocks would there be?

_____

_____

_____

6. Which is a rule for the table below?

In	3	9	4	7
Out	7	13	8	11

A Add 4

B Multiply 2

C Multiply 4

D Add 5

Problem Solving: Act It Out and Use Reasoning

Izzie has 12 coins. Four of the coins are quarters. He has 2 more dimes than nickels. How many of each coin does he have?

You can use logical reasoning to find the answer. You may be able to determine information that is not told.

What do I know?	What do I need to find out?	What can I determine from the information?
Izzie has 12 coins. 4 of the coins are quarters. Izzie has 2 more dimes than nickels.	How many dimes does Izzie have? How many nickels does Izzie have?	If 4 of the 12 coins are quarters, Izzie has a total of 8 dimes and nickels.

You can act it out to find how many dimes and nickels Izzie has.

Take 8 two-color counters. Find combinations so that one color will have 2 more than the other. If you try 4 and 4, the difference is 0, so try 5 and 3. It works.

So, Izzie has 4 quarters, 5 dimes, and 3 nickels.

Solve. Find the number of each kind of object in the collection.

1. Kim's Music Video Collection

13 videos in all
4 concert videos
3 more rap videos than pop videos

Concert videos = ☐

Rap videos = ☐

Pop videos = ☐

2. Molly's Art Collection

5 paintings
3 more sculptures than mosaics
16 pieces in all

Paintings = ☐

Sculptures = ☐

Mosaics = ☐

Name _____

Problem Solving: Act It Out and Use Reasoning

Ask Yourself...
What do I know?
What do I need
to find out?

Solve. Find the number of each kind of object in the collection.

1. Sue's Card Collection

8 packs of baseball cards
3 fewer packs of hockey cards
than football cards
17 packs in all

Baseball cards = ☐

Hockey cards = ☐

Football cards = ☐

2. Drew's DVD Collection

7 comedy DVDs
4 more drama DVDs than horror
DVDs
15 DVDs in all

Comedy DVDs = ☐

Drama DVDs = ☐

Horror DVDs = ☐

3. Strategy Practice Mike is 8 years older than Kyle. Kyle is 6 years old. The sum of Mike's, Kyle's, and Jamal's ages is 23. How many years old is Jamal?

_____

4. Miranda has 24 CDs in her collection. Of those CDs, 10 are pop CDs. She has 6 more country CDs than jazz CDs. How many country CDs does Miranda have?

_____

5. Curt has 12 models in all. Three of the models are airplanes. Curt has 5 more models of cars than boats. How many models of cars does Curt have?

_____

6. Stevie, Lindsey, and Christine are the lead singers in a band. They will sing 18 songs. Lindsey will sing 8 songs. Christine will sing 6 fewer songs than Stevie. How many songs will Stevie sing?

A 2   **B** 4   **C** 6   **D** 8

Name _____

Subtracting Across Zeros

Here is how to subtract across zeros.

Find 606 − 377.

Estimate: 600 − 400 = 200

Step 1	**Step 2**	**Step 3**	**Step 4**
606 − 377	5 10 6̶0̶6̶ − 377	9 5 1̶0̶ 16 6̶0̶6̶ − 377	9 5 1̶0̶ 16 6̶0̶6̶ − 377 ‾‾‾‾‾ 229
You cannot subtract 7 ones from 6 ones, so you must regroup.	Since there is a zero in the tens place, you must regroup using the hundreds. Regroup 6 hundreds as 5 hundreds and 10 tens.	Regroup 10 tens and 6 ones as 9 tens and 16 ones.	Subtract. 1 1 229 + 377 ‾‾‾‾‾ 606 You can check your answer by using addition.

Subtract.

1.   707
      −   58

2.   950
      −   47

3.   800
      − 638

4.   3,506
      −   866

5.   4,507
      − 3,569

6.   3,076
      − 1,466

7.   8,106
      − 2,999

8.   6,083
      − 1,492

9. Reasonableness Lexi subtracts 9,405 from 11,138. Should her answer be greater than or less than 2,000? Explain.

_____

_____

Name _____

Subtracting Across Zeros

Subtract.

1.   906
     −   45

2.   3,091
     − 1,361

3.   4,000
     − 2,557

4.   800
     −   139

5.   1,070
     −   593

6.   8,904
     − 3,596

7.   3,007
     − 2,366

8.   523
     −   203

9. 7,403 − 3,254   **10.** 5,067 − 2,987   **11.** 6,790 − 1,298

_____   _____   _____

12. Robert set a goal to swim 1,000 laps in the local
swimming pool during his summer break. Robert has
currently finished 642 laps. How many more laps
does he have to swim in order to meet his goal?

A 332   **B** 358   **C** 468   **D** 472

13. **Writing to Explain** If 694 − 72 = _____, then 622 + _____ = 694.
Explain the process of checking your work.

_____

_____

_____

_____

Problem Solving: Draw a Picture and Write an Equation

Read the question and follow the steps to develop a problem-solving strategy.

In the morning, a grocery store had 28 apples on display. By the end of the day, 11 apples had been purchased. How many apples were left?

Step 1: Read/Understand

- Find the information you are given. [There were 28 apples; now there are 11 fewer apples.]

- Find the information you need to figure out. [The number of apples that are left]

Step 2: Plan

- Draw a picture that helps you visualize the problem you are trying to solve.

28 in all

11	?

Step 3: Solve

- Figure out which operation you need to use to solve the problem, and write an equation. [Subtraction; $28 - 11 = ?$]

- Solve the equation to answer the problem. [$28 - 11 = 17$; 17 apples were left.]

1. **Strategy Practice** On Monday, Erika put 12 flakes of fish food in her fish tank before school, and 13 more when she got home. How many flakes did she put in the tank that day? Use the steps to answer the question. _____

Step 1:

- What information are you given?

- What information do you need to figure out?

Step 2:

- Draw a picture.

Step 3:

- Choose an operation and write an equation.

- Solve the equation.

Solve the following problems. Draw pictures to help you.

2. Roy is reading a book that is 68 pages. He has read 24 pages so far. How many more pages does he have to read to finish the book? _____

3. There are 29 students in the school band. During practice, 6 new students joined the band. How many students are in the band now? _____

4. Jaycee's teacher gave her a box of 96 pens. She gave 17 of the pens to her classmates. How many pens were left in the box? _____

Name _____

Problem Solving: Draw a Picture and Write an Equation

For exercises **1** through **4** write an equation and solve. Use the picture to help you.

1. A remote control car has a speed of 5 feet per second. How many feet will the car travel in 6 seconds?

_____

2. Danny has 45 minutes to take a math test. If Danny finishes half the test in 19 minutes, how many minutes does he have left to finish it?

_____

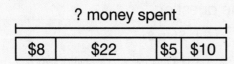

3. While shopping, Janet bought a shirt for $8, a pair of jeans for $22, mittens for $5, and a hat for $10. How much money did Janet spend?

_____

? money spent			
$8	$22	$5	$10

4. The 175th anniversary of the completion of the Erie Canal was in the year 2000. If it took 8 years to dig the canal, in what year did the digging of the Erie Canal begin?

_____

Year 2000		
175	8	? year digging began

5. The average length of a song on a certain CD is 3 minutes. The CD has 12 songs. Write an equation for the length of the whole CD. Draw a picture to help you.

A 12×3 **B** $12 + 3$ **C** $12 \div 3$ **D** $12 - 3$

6. Writing to Explain It takes Jinny 56 minutes to drive to her friend's house. She drove 15 minutes and then stopped at a store. She then drove another 10 minutes. What do you need to do to find the amount of time she has left to drive?

_____

_____

_____

Arrays and Multiplying by 10 and 100

You can use addition to help you multiply.

Find 3 × 10.

There are three groups of 10.

Add 10 three times
10 + 10 + 10 = 30
          or
Multiply 3 groups of 10.
3 × 10 = 30

Find 3 × 100.

There are three groups of 100.

Add 100 three times.
100 + 100 + 100 = 300
          or
Multiply 3 groups of 100.
3 × 100 = 300

Find each product.

1. Find 4 × 10.

Add: 10 + 10 + 10 + 10 = _____

So, 4 × 10 = _____.

2. Find 2 × 100.

Add: 100 + 100 = _____

So, 2 × 100 = _____.

3. Reasonableness Michael used addition to find 9 × 100 and he said the product was 90. What did he do wrong?

_____

4. Draw two sets of arrays to represent 6 × 10 and 5 × 100. Then show how to use addition to find each product.

Name _____

Arrays and Multiplying by 10 and 100

Find each product.

1. 5 × 10 = _____

2. 2 × 100 = _____

3. 3 × 10 = _____

4. 3 × 100 = _____

5. 6 × 10 = _____

6. 5 × 100 = _____

7. Reasoning What whole number could you use to complete
☐ × 100 = ☐00 so that ☐00 is greater than 400 but less
than 600?

_____

8. Mr. James does 100 sit-ups every morning. How many
sit-ups will he do in 7 days?

A 70   **B** 100   **C** 107   **D** 700

9. Writing to Explain Jackie has 10 groups of pennies with
3 pennies in each group. Carlos has 5 groups of pennies with
100 pennies in each group. Who has more pennies? Explain
how you know.

_____

_____

_____

_____

Multiplying by Multiples of 10 and 100

Patterns can help you multiply by numbers that are multiples of 10 or 100.

$3 \times 5 = 15$	$2 \times 4 = 8$	$5 \times 7 = 35$
$3 \times 50 = 150$	$2 \times 40 = 80$	$5 \times 70 = 350$
$3 \times 500 = 1,500$	$2 \times 400 = 800$	$5 \times 700 = 3,500$

To find each of the products above, first complete the basic multiplication fact. Then write the same number of zeros seen in the factor that is a multiple of 10. If the product ends in a zero, the answer will have an extra zero. For example:

Find 4×500.

First find 4×5.   **$4 \times 5 = 20$**

Then, count the number of zeros
in the multiple of 100.   **500 has 2 zeros.**

Write 2 zeros after the product
of the basic multiplication fact.
So, there are 3 zeros in the product.   **2,000**

Find each product. Use mental math.

1. $8 \times 80 =$ _____

2. $6 \times 60 =$ _____

3. $7 \times 90 =$ _____

4. $5 \times 200 =$ _____

5. $3 \times 40 =$ _____

6. $7 \times 200 =$ _____

7. $500 \times 6 =$ _____

8. $600 \times 9 =$ _____

9. $3 \times 800 =$ _____

10. $600 \times 7 =$ _____

11. Number Sense To find 8×600, multiply 8 and 6, then write ___ zeros to form the product.

Multiplying by Multiples of 10 and 100

Find each product. Use mental math.

1. $6 \times 70 =$ _____

2. $80 \times 2 =$ _____

3. $40 \times 9 =$ _____

4. $20 \times 3 =$ _____

5. $4 \times 500 =$ _____

6. $300 \times 9 =$ _____

7. $8 \times 600 =$ _____

8. $7 \times 400 =$ _____

9. $6 \times 200 =$ _____

10. $800 \times 5 =$ _____

11. $6 \times 800 =$ _____

12. $400 \times 3 =$ _____

13. Number Sense How many zeros will the product of 7×500 have? _____

Mr. Young has 30 times as many pencils as Jack. The whole school has 200 times as many pencils as Jack. If Jack has 2 pencils, how many pencils do the following have?

14. Mr. Young?

15. The whole school?

_____   _____

16. Find 3×400.

    A 120   **B** 1,200   **C** 12,000   **D** 120,000

17. Writing to Explain Wendi says that the product of 5×400 will have 2 zeros. Is she correct? Explain.

_____

_____

_____

Name _____

Breaking Apart to Multiply

You can make multiplication easier by breaking larger numbers apart by place value.

Find 3 × 35.

Break apart 35 into 30 + 5.

Multiply the tens.

3 × 30 = 90

Multiply the ones.

3 × 5 = 15

Add the partial products: 90 + 15 = 105

So, 3 × 35 = 105.

Complete.

1. 5 × 23

5 × 20 = ☐

5 × 3 = ☐

☐ + ☐ = ☐

2. 4 × 246

4 × 200 = ☐

4 × 40 = ☐

4 × 6 = ☐

☐ + ☐ + ☐ = ☐

Find each product. You may use place-value blocks or drawings to help.

3. 6 × 21 = _____

4. 5 × 43 = _____

5. 3 × 116 = _____

6. 5 × 22 = _____

7. 3 × 352 = _____

8. 7 × 226 = _____

9. 4 × 34 = _____

10. 6 × 217 = _____

11. Number Sense Tim said, "To find 6 × 33, I can add 18 + 18."
Do you agree with Tim? Why or why not?

_____

Name _____

Breaking Apart to Multiply

Find each product. You may use place-value blocks or draw a picture to help.

1. 4 × 43   **2.** 7 × 218   **3.** 5 × 13   **4.** 2 × 88   **5.** 4 × 334

_____   _____   _____   _____   _____

6. 3 × 49   **7.** 6 × 42   **8.** 4 × 156   **9.** 3 × 25   **10.** 5 × 224

_____   _____   _____   _____   _____

11. 2 × 54   **12.** 4 × 337   **13.** 7 × 22   **14.** 5 × 216   **15.** 6 × 137

_____   _____   _____   _____   _____

16. A carpenter makes chairs with slats that run across the back of the chairs as shown. Each chair uses 7 slats. He needs to make 24 chairs. How many slats must he make?

Slats

_____

17. Each wood panel is 6 feet wide. Exactly 19 panels are needed to cover the walls of a room. How many feet of wood panels are needed?

_____

18. Which is equal to 5 × 25?

A (5 × 5) + (2 × 5)   **C** 5 × 20

B (5 × 20) + (5 × 1)   **D** (5 × 20) + (5 × 5)

19. Writing to Explain How can you multiply 242 × 8 by breaking apart numbers?

_____

_____

_____

Using Mental Math to Multiply

You can multiply mentally by using compensation.

Find 4 × 19 using compensation.

Step 1: Substitute a number for 19 that is easy to multiply by 4.

    4 × 19
      ↓   Add 1 to make 20.
    4 × 20

Step 2: Find the new product.

    4 × 20 = 80

Step 3: Now adjust. Subtract 4 groups of 1.

    80 − 4 = 76

So, 4 × 19 = 76.

Find 6 × 205 using compensation.

Step 1: Substitute a number for 205 that is easy to multiply by 6.

    6 × 205
      ↓   Subtract 5
    6 × 200   to make 200.

Step 2: Find the new product.

    6 × 200 = 1,200

Step 3: Now adjust. Add 6 groups of 5.

    1,200 + 30 = 1,230

So, 6 × 205 = 1,230.

Use compensation to find each product.

1. 5 × 32 = _____

2. 195 × 5 = _____

3. 7 × 53 = _____

4. 66 × 2 = _____

5. 6 × 497 = _____

6. 92 × 4 = _____

7. 603 × 3 = _____

8. 31 × 8 = _____

9. 598 × 5 = _____

10. 4 × 29 = _____

11. 4 × 199 = _____

12. 310 × 6 = _____

13. Algebra In $a \times 60 = 120$, a is a one-digit number. What number does a represent?

_____

Using Mental Math to Multiply

Use compensation to find each product.

1. $34 \times 4 =$ _____

2. $199 \times 6 =$ _____

3. $53 \times 7 =$ _____

4. $505 \times 4 =$ _____

5. $41 \times 6 =$ _____

6. $298 \times 6 =$ _____

7. $76 \times 5 =$ _____

8. $803 \times 7 =$ _____

9. $83 \times 3 =$ _____

10. $390 \times 2 =$ _____

11. $28 \times 8 =$ _____

12. $709 \times 4 =$ _____

13. $94 \times 2 =$ _____

14. $410 \times 8 =$ _____

15. $16 \times 4 =$ _____

16. $197 \times 5 =$ _____

17. $46 \times 5 =$ _____

18. $896 \times 9 =$ _____

19. Reasonableness Quinn used compensation to find the product of 37×4. First, she found $40 \times 4 = 160$. Then she adjusted that product by adding 3 groups of 4 to get her final answer of 172. What did she do incorrectly?

_____

_____

_____

20. Davidson's Bakery uses 9 dozen eggs to make cookies each day. There are twelve eggs in one dozen. How many eggs do they use?

A 90   **B** 98   **C** 108   **D** 112

21. Writing to Explain Find the product of 503×6. Explain how you found the product.

_____

_____

Using Rounding to Estimate

You can use rounding to estimate products.

Use rounding to estimate 7 × 28.

First, round 28 to the nearest ten.
28 rounds to 30.

Then, multiply.
7 × 30 = 210

So, 7 × 28 is about 210.

Use rounding to estimate 7 × 215.

First, round 215 to the nearest hundred.
215 rounds to 200.

Then, multiply.
7 × 200 = 1,400

So, 7 × 215 is about 1,400.

Estimate each product.

1. 6 × 88 is close to 6 × _____

2. 279 × 4 is close to _____ × 4

3. 7 × 31 _____

4. 38 × 5 _____

5. 21 × 6 _____

6. 3 × 473 _____

7. 5 × 790 _____

8. 488 × 6 _____

9. Number Sense Estimate to determine if 5 × 68 is greater than or less than 350. Tell how you decided.

_____

_____

10. Estimate how many of Part C would be made in 4 months.

_____

11. Estimate how many of Part B would be made in 3 months.

_____

12. Estimate how many of Part A would be made in 9 months.

_____

Parts Made at a Factory in One Month

Using Rounding to Estimate

Estimate each product.

1. 38 × 2 _____

2. 7 × 47 _____

3. 54 × 6 _____

4. 121 × 2 _____

5. 578 × 8 _____

6. 823 × 3 _____

7. 7 × 289 _____

8. 183 × 4 _____

9. 2 × 87 _____

10. 673 × 8 _____

The distance between Bill's house and his aunt's house
is 835 miles.

11. About how many miles would
he drive if he made 4 one-way
trips?

_____

12. About how many miles would
he drive if he made 9 one-way trips?

_____

13. Vera has 8 boxes of paper clips. Each box contains
275 paper clips. About how many paper clips does Vera have?

A 240   **B** 1,600   **C** 2,400   **D** 24,000

14. Writing to Explain A large 7-story office building has
116 windows on each floor. About how many windows does
the building have in all? Explain.

_____

_____

_____

_____

Problem Solving: Reasonableness

After you solve a problem, it is important to check your answer to see whether it is reasonable.

Read and Understand

There are 5 animals on a farm. Each animal eats 105 pounds of food per week. How much food does the farmer have to buy each week?

? pounds of food in all

105	105	105	105	105

Plan and Solve

Use breaking apart or compensation to find 5×105.
$5 \times 105 = 525$

Check for Reasonableness

First, ask yourself, "Did I answer the right question?" Then, estimate to check your answer. $5 \times 100 = 500$. The answer is reasonable because 500 is close to 525.

Solve the following problems. Check your answers for reasonableness.

1. Marisa says $302 \times 6 = 192$.
   Explain why Marisa's answer is not reasonable.

   _____

   _____

   _____

2. Jaime practiced swimming for about 11 hours every week for 8 weeks. About how many hours did he practice in all? How can you check your answer?

   _____

   _____

   _____

Problem Solving: Reasonableness

For **1** and **2**, use reasonableness to decide if each answer is correct. Explain why the answer is reasonable or not. If the answer is incorrect, give the correct answer.

1. Johan is selling baseball cards for 12¢ each. He is selling 8 cards and says he'll make $8.

_____

_____

2. Erika wants to give 5 stickers to everyone in her class. Her class sits in 4 rows of 7, and Erika says she'll need 140 stickers.

_____

_____

3. Viktor has 7 piles of coins with 63 coins in each. Which is a reasonable number of coins in Viktor's piles?

    A 300, because 7 × 63 is about 7 × 40 = 280.

    B 360, because 7 × 63 is about 7 × 50 = 350.

    C 441, because 7 × 63 is about 7 × 60 = 420.

    D 500, because 7 × 63 is about 7 × 70 = 490.

Julie planted a sunflower and kept track of its height in a table. Use the table to solve **4** and **5**.

4. How tall will the sunflower be after the 5th week if it continues to grow at the same rate?

_____

5. **Writing to Explain** The world's largest sunflower was about 300 inches tall. Julie says her sunflower will be that tall after 3 months. Is Julie's answer reasonable? Explain why or why not. (Remember, there are about 4 weeks in one month.)

Height of Sunflower	
Week	**Height in Inches**
1	16
2	32
3	48
4	64
5	

_____

Name _____

Arrays and Using an Expanded Algorithm

You can use arrays of place-value blocks to multiply.

Find the product for 3 × 14.

What You Show	What You Write
3 × 10 = 30　　　3 × 4 = 12 30 + 12 = 42	$\begin{array}{r} 14 \\ \times\ 3 \\ \hline 12 \\ +\ 30 \\ \hline 42 \end{array}$　　3 X 4 ones 　　　3 X 1 ten

Draw an array for each problem to find the partial products and the product. Complete the calculation.

1.　　18
　　× 4

2.　　21
　　× 6

3.　　17
　　× 6

4.　　11
　　× 2

5.　　23
　　× 5

6.　　16
　　× 3

7. **Number Sense** What two simpler problems can you use to find 9 × 38? (Hint: Think about the tens and ones.)

Name _____

Arrays and Using an Expanded Algorithm

Use the array to find the partial products. Add the partial products to find the product.

1. 42
   × 8

2. 39
   × 7

3. 21
   × 4

4. 27
   × 6

5. 7 × 14 = _____

6. 3 × 52 = _____

7. 4 × 42 = _____

8. 5 × 26 = _____

9. 6 × 62 = _____

10. 9 × 76 = _____

11. Alex can type 72 words per minute. How many
    words can Alex type in 5 minutes?   _____

12. Find 8 × 44.

    A 282   B 312   C 352   D 372

13. **Writing to Explain** Explain how you can use an array to
    find partial products for 4 × 36.

    _____

    _____

    _____

P 6·1

Connecting the Expanded and Standard Algorithms

There are different ways to find the product for 3×45.

Expanded Algorithm	Standard Algorithm	
Find the partial products. $\begin{array}{r} 45 \\ \times\ 3 \\ \hline 15 \\ +\ 120 \\ \hline 135 \end{array}$	$\begin{array}{r} \boxed{1}\quad \\ 45 \\ \times\ 3 \\ \hline 13\boxed{5} \end{array}$	Multiply ones. 3×5 ones = 15 ones Regroup if needed. 15 ones = 1 ten 5 ones Multiply tens. 3×4 tens = 12 tens Add any extra tens. $12 + 1 = 13$ tens Write 13 tens as 1 hundred 3 tens.

Solve.

1. **Draw a Picture** Find 4×35 using the expanded algorithm and then the standard algorithm.

2. At his job, Mr. Miller works 7 hours a day, Monday through Friday. How many hours does he work in 2 weeks?

   _____

3. **Think About the Process** Write the multiplication problem that matches the picture below. Then use the standard algorithm to find the product.

   _____

4. **Writing to Explain** Stella used the expanded algorithm to find the product for 9×39. Her work is shown below. Is she correct? Explain.

   $\begin{array}{r} 39 \\ \times\ 9 \\ \hline 270 \\ +\ 81 \\ \hline 351 \end{array}$

   _____

   _____

   _____

   _____

Connecting the Expanded and Standard Algorithms

For **1** through **4**, use the expanded algorithm to multiply.

1.
```
    83
×    4
```

partial product
partial product
product

2.
```
    57
×    6
```
partial product
partial product
product

3.
```
    19
×    8
```

4.
```
    42
×    9
```

For **5** through **10**, use the standard algorithm to multiply.

5.
```
    75
×    6
```

6.
```
    64
×    5
```

7.
```
    17
×    9
```

8.
```
    93
×    4
```

9.
```
    28
×    7
```

10.
```
    56
×    8
```

11. A commuter van has 38 seats and 14 windows. How many windows are in 6 commuter vans?

A 70   **B** 84   **C** 102   **D** 228

12. **Writing to Explain** Suppose you had to find 4 × 57. How are the expanded algorithm and the standard algorithm alike? How are they different?

_____

_____

_____

_____

Name _____

Multiplying 2-Digit by 1-Digit Numbers

Here is how to multiply a 2-digit number by a 1-digit number using paper and pencil.

Find 3 × 24.	What You Think	What You Write
Step 1 Multiply the ones. Regroup if necessary.	3 × 4 = 12 ones Regroup 12 ones as 1 ten 2 ones.	$$\begin{array}{r} 1 \\ 24 \\ \times\ 3 \\ \hline 2 \end{array}$$
Step 2 Multiply the tens. Add any extra tens.	3 × 2 tens = 6 tens 6 tens + 1 ten = 7 tens	$$\begin{array}{r} 1 \\ 24 \\ \times\ 3 \\ \hline 72 \end{array}$$

Is your answer reasonable?

   Exact answer: 3 × 24 = 72

   Think: 24 is close to 25.

   Estimate: 3 × 25 = 75   Since 72 is close to 75, the answer is reasonable.

Find each product. Estimate to check reasonableness.

1. $\begin{array}{r} 13 \\ \times\ 3 \\ \hline \end{array}$

2. $\begin{array}{r} 17 \\ \times\ 7 \\ \hline \end{array}$

3. $\begin{array}{r} 24 \\ \times\ 5 \\ \hline \end{array}$

4. $\begin{array}{r} 48 \\ \times\ 8 \\ \hline \end{array}$

5. $\begin{array}{r} 62 \\ \times\ 6 \\ \hline \end{array}$

6. $\begin{array}{r} 36 \\ \times\ 5 \\ \hline \end{array}$

7. $\begin{array}{r} 88 \\ \times\ 5 \\ \hline \end{array}$

8. $\begin{array}{r} 52 \\ \times\ 8 \\ \hline \end{array}$

9. Estimation Use estimation to decide which has the greater product: 81 × 6 or 79 × 5.   _____

Multiplying 2-Digit by 1-Digit Numbers

Find each product. Estimate to check reasonableness.

1.
```
    1 9
  ×   4
  _____
  7 □
```

2.
```
    2 3
  ×   7
  _____
  □ 6 □
```

3.
```
    5 1
  ×   6
  _____
  □ 0 □
```

4.
```
   39
  × 7
```

5.
```
   48
  × 5
```

6.
```
   53
  × 7
```

7.
```
   29
  × 8
```

8. 42 × 6 = _____

9. 89 × 8 = _____

10. 77 × 9 = _____

11. 94 × 4 = _____

12. Number Sense Penny says that 4 × 65 = 260. Estimate to check Penny's answer. Is she right? Explain.

_____

_____

13. A large dump truck uses about 18 gallons of fuel for 1 hour of work. About how many gallons of fuel are needed if the truck works for 5 hours? _____

14. Which of the following is a reasonable estimate for 6 × 82?

A 48   **B** 480   **C** 540   **D** 550

15. Writing to Explain Tyrone has 6 times as many marbles as his sister Pam. Pam has 34 marbles. Louis has 202 marbles. Who has more marbles, Tyrone or Louis? Explain how you found your answer.

_____

_____

Multiplying 3- and 4-Digit by 1-Digit Numbers

The steps below show how to multiply greater numbers.

	Example A	Example B
Step 1 Multiply the ones. Regroup if necessary.	1 154 × 4 ――― 6	2 1,214 × 7 ――― 8
Step 2 Multiply the tens. Add any extra tens. Regroup if necessary.	21 154 × 4 ――― 16	2 1,214 × 7 ――― 98
Step 3 Multiply the hundreds. Add any extra hundreds.	21 154 × 4 ――― 616	1 2 1,214 × 7 ――― 498
Step 4 Multiply the thousands. Add any extra thousands.		1 2 1,214 × 7 ――― 8,498

Find each product. Estimate to check reasonableness.

1.   185
     × 4

2.   517
     × 4

3.   2,741
     × 3

4.   413
     × 6

5.   2,625
     × 6

6.   812
     × 5

7.   3,711
     × 8

8.   1,381
     × 5

9. Molly and her sister each have 118 shells. How many shells do they have all together?

10. A factory can make 2,418 footballs in 1 week. How many can it make in 9 weeks?

Name _____

Multiplying 3- and 4-Digit by 1-Digit Numbers

Find each product. Estimate to check reasonableness.

1. 352
    × 3

2. 2,768
    × 7

3. 482
    × 8

4. 3,521
    × 4

5. 4,219
    × 6

6. 385
    × 4

7. 632
    × 5

8. 1,848
    × 9

9. 7 × 2,117 = _____

10. 6 × 517 = _____

For **11** and **12**, use the table at the right.

11. If Player A scores the same number of runs each season, how many runs will he score in 5 seasons?

_____

Runs Scored in 2010

Player	Runs Scored
A	128
B	113
C	142

12. If Player C scores the same number of runs each season, how many runs will he score in 8 seasons?

_____

13. How many bottles of water would Tim sell if he sold 1,734 bottles each week for 4 weeks?

    A 5,886　　**B** 6,836　　**C** 6,928　　**D** 6,936

14. If you know that 8 × 300 = 2,400, how can you find 8 × 320? Explain.

_____

_____

_____

Multiplying by 1-Digit Numbers

Follow the steps below to multiply by a 1-digit number.
Find the product of 3 × 2,576.

① Multiply the ones: 3 × 6 ones = 18 ones.
 Regroup as 1 ten and 8 ones.

② Multiply the tens: 3 × 7 tens = 21 tens.
 Add 1 regrouped ten; 22 tens.
 Regroup as 2 hundreds and 2 tens.

③ Multiply the hundreds: 3 × 5 hundreds = 15 hundreds.
 Add 2 regrouped hundreds; 17 hundreds.
 Regroup as 1 thousand and 7 hundreds.

④ Multiply the thousands: 3 × 2 thousands = 6 thousands.
 Add 1 regrouped thousand; 7 thousands.

Complete the table. The first row has been done for you.

Find the product.	Estimate the product.	Find the exact product.	Is it reasonable?
1. 7 × 66	7 × 70 = 490	$\begin{array}{r} 4 \\ 66 \\ \times\ 7 \\ \hline 462 \end{array}$	⨯ Yes ___ No
2. 8 × 93	____ × ____ = ____		___ Yes ___ No
3. 6 × 875	____ × ____ = ____		___ Yes ___ No
4. 3 × 486	____ × ____ = ____		___ Yes ___ No
5. 4 × 7,821	___ × ____ = ____		___ Yes ___ No
6. 5 × 3,111	___ × ____ = ____		___ Yes ___ No

7. **Number Sense** Margo found that 3 × 741 = 2,223. How
 could you use mental math to find the product of 6 × 741?

_____

_____

Multiplying by 1-Digit Numbers

Find each product. Estimate to check reasonableness.

1. $\begin{array}{r} 49 \\ \times\ 3 \\ \hline \end{array}$

2. $\begin{array}{r} 87 \\ \times\ 5 \\ \hline \end{array}$

3. $\begin{array}{r} 726 \\ \times\ 9 \\ \hline \end{array}$

4. $\begin{array}{r} 518 \\ \times\ 4 \\ \hline \end{array}$

5. $7 \times 3{,}258 =$ _____

6. $8 \times 1{,}096 =$ _____

7. $2 \times 4{,}615 =$ _____

8. $3 \times 2{,}934 =$ _____

9. It takes thousands of separate drawings to make a cartoon movie. Cartoons "move" because each drawing passes by so quickly. If 1,440 drawings go by in 1 minute, how many drawings are needed for a 7-minute cartoon?

10. The Plaza Cine-Plex has 6 movie theaters. Each theater has 452 seats. How many seats does the Plaza Cine-Plex have in all?

    A 2,721   C 2,708

    B 2,712   D 2,522

Use the price chart at the right to answer 11 through 14.

11. How much more do 5 cordless drills cost than 4 belt sanders?

Power Tool	Price
Circular saw	$129
Belt sander	$247
Cordless drill	$206

12. **Number Sense** A carpenter has $1,000 to spend on power tools. Can she afford to buy 5 cordless drills? Explain.

13. Jacob bought a new circular saw. Then he bought 8 different blades for it. Each blade cost $23. How much did Jacob spend in all?

14. **Writing to Explain** Aaron has a woodworking shop. He wants to buy 2 of each of the tools shown in the table. What is the total cost? Explain.

Problem Solving:
Missing or Extra Information

Some problems contain too much or too little information. If a problem has missing information, you cannot solve it. If a problem has extra information, you need to figure out what information is needed to solve the problem.

Step 1: Read and Understand

Ramon is 6 feet tall. The average male giraffe is 3 times as tall as Ramon and weighs about 1,800 pounds. How tall is the average male giraffe?

To solve this problem, you need to find how tall the average male giraffe is.

Step 2: Plan and Solve

Decide which information you need to solve the problem and what is extra information.

You need to know how tall Ramon is to find the height of the average male giraffe. You do not need the weight of the giraffe to answer the question. Multiply 3 by Ramon's height.

$$3 \times 6 = 18$$

The average male giraffe is about 18 feet tall.

Nora has a collection of 14 stuffed animals. Her collection includes bears, lions, cats, and penguins. Mindy has twice as many stuffed animals as Nora.

1. Do you have enough information to find out how many stuffed animals Mindy has? Explain.

   _____

   _____

2. What information did you not use to solve this problem?

   _____

   _____

3. How many stuffed animals does Mindy have?

   _____

Problem Solving:
Missing or Extra Information

For **1** through **3**, decide if each problem has extra information or not enough information. Tell any information that is not needed or that is missing. Solve if you have enough information.

1. Kendall pitches for his school's baseball team. Every game Kendall pitches, he gets about 5 strikeouts. Each game is about 2 hours. If Kendall pitches in 7 games during the season, how many strikeouts will he have?

   _____

2. **Geometry** Sandra is putting up a fence around her garden, which is in the shape of a square. Each foot of fencing costs $9. If each side of the fence will be 8 feet long, how many feet of fencing will Sandra need?

   _____

3. Gretchen sings and plays guitar in a band after school. If Gretchen sings half of the songs the band knows, how many songs does the band know?

   _____

4. What do you need to know if you are trying to find the year George Washington was born and you know he died in 1799?

   A The current year

   B The exact date he died

   C How old he was when he died

   D There is not enough information

5. **Writing to Explain** If you wanted to write a word problem about how much money the fourth-grade class collected at their bake sale, what information would you need to include?

   _____

Name _____

Arrays and Multiplying 2-Digit Numbers by Multiples of 10

You can use an array to find the product of 20×32.

Think: 20 groups of 30 + 20 groups of 2

20 groups of 30 = 600

20 groups of 2 = 40

600 + 40 = 640

So, $20 \times 32 = 640$.

20 groups of 30 = 600   20 groups of 2 = 40

Find each product.

1. 10×12

10 groups of 10 = _____

10 groups of 2 = _____

_____ + _____ = _____

So, $10 \times 12 =$ _____.

2. 20×18

20 groups of 10 = _____

20 groups of 8 = _____

_____ + _____ = _____

So, $20 \times 18 =$ _____.

Use models to find each product.

3. 40×16 _____

4. 30×34 _____

5. Writing to Explain Describe what an array that shows 70×35 would look like. How many rows would there be? How many items would be in each row?

_____

_____

Arrays and Multiplying 2-Digit Numbers by Multiples of 10

Find each product.

1. 10 × 34 = _____

2. 20 × 42 = _____

Draw an array to find each product.

3. 40 × 24 = _____

4. 30 × 33 = _____

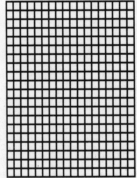

5. The array at the right can be used to find the product of two numbers. What are the two numbers?

_____

6. It takes about 40 gallons of water to do a load of wash. How many gallons of water does it take to do 15 loads of wash?

A 400   **B** 415   **C** 600   **D** 900

7. Writing to Explain The art teacher has 30 boxes of crayons with 16 crayons in each box. She gives 10 of the boxes to students to use. Explain how to find how many crayons she has left.

_____

_____

Name _____

Using Mental Math to Multiply 2-Digit Numbers

You can multiply with mental math by using basic facts and patterns.

Example A: $5 \times 5 = 25$

   $5 \times 50 = 250$

The product contains the number of zeros in each factor.

Example B: $5 \times 6 = 30$

   $5 \times 60 = 300$

   $50 \times 60 = 3,000$

When the product of a basic fact includes a zero, there is an extra zero in the product.

Multiply. Use mental math.

1. $20 \times 20 =$

2. $50 \times 10 =$

3. $40 \times 40 =$

_____

_____

_____

4. $30 \times 80 =$

5. $60 \times 60 =$

6. $50 \times 90 =$

_____

_____

_____

7. $70 \times 30 =$

8. $70 \times 60 =$

9. $40 \times 50 =$

_____

_____

_____

10. Tell what numbers go in the blanks.

To find 90×30, multiply _____ and _____.

Then write _____ zeros at the end.

Using Mental Math to Multiply 2-Digit Numbers

Multiply. Use mental math.

1. $40 \times 30 =$ _____

2. $50 \times 90 =$ _____

3. $90 \times 20 =$ _____

4. $60 \times 50 =$ _____

5. $30 \times 60 =$ _____

6. $40 \times 60 =$ _____

7. $90 \times 70 =$ _____

8. $70 \times 40 =$ _____

9. $50 \times 80 =$ _____

10. $30 \times 80 =$ _____

11. $90 \times 50 =$ _____

12. $50 \times 40 =$ _____

13. How many zeros are in the product of 60×90? Explain how you know.

_____

_____

Student A can type 40 words in one minute. Student B can type 30 words in one minute.

14. How many words can Student A type in 20 minutes? _____

15. How many words can Student B type in 30 minutes? _____

16. How many words can Student A type in 60 minutes?

A 240   **B** 2,400   **C** 24,000   **D** 240,000

17. Writing to Explain There are 30 players on each high school football team. Explain how you can find the total number of players if there are 40 teams.

_____

_____

Using Rounding to Estimate

Use rounding to estimate 28 × 36.

Step 1
Round each number to the nearest 10.

- Look at the digit in the ones place. Since it is greater than 5, add 1 to the digit in the rounding place.

- Change the digit to the right of the rounding place to 0.

28 rounds to 30 and 36 rounds to 40.

28 × 36
↓   ↓
30 × 40

Step 2
Multiply 30 × 40.

30 × 40 = 1,200

So, 28 × 36 is about 1,200.

Use rounding to estimate each product.

1. 31 × 12

31 rounds to _____.

12 rounds to _____.

_____ × _____ = _____

2. 28 × 17

28 rounds to _____.

17 rounds to _____.

_____ × _____ = _____

3. 46 × 13 = _____

4. 52 × 42 = _____

5. 42 × 18 = _____

6. 38 × 36 = _____

7. 48 × 59 = _____

8. 71 × 34 = _____

9. 62 × 82 = _____

10. 95 × 21 = _____

11. The school store has 25 packages of erasers. There are 12 erasers in each package. About how many erasers does the school store have for sale?

_____

12. Chris estimated the product of 37 and 86 by multiplying 40 × 90. Tell how you know if this is greater than or less than the actual product.

_____

_____

Using Rounding to Estimate

Use rounding to estimate each product.

1. 38 × 13 = _____   **2.** 41 × 18 = _____   **3.** 54 × 14 = _____

4. 44 × 22 = _____   **5.** 45 × 19 = _____   **6.** 34 × 48 = _____

7. 39 × 37 = _____   **8.** 25 × 81 = _____   **9.** 51 × 39 = _____

10. 48 × 29 = _____   **11.** 71 × 63 = _____   **12.** 82 × 54 = _____

13. A deep-sea fisherman went fishing 14 times last month. He caught 28 fish each time. About how many fish did he catch all together last month?

_____

14. Alligators lay between 20 and 50 eggs in a nest. A park ranger in Everglades National Park counted the number of eggs in 28 nests. On average, there were 40 eggs in each nest. About how many eggs did he count?

A 80   **C** 800

B 120   **D** 1,200

15. **Writing to Explain** Eric estimated 28 × 48 by finding 30 × 50. His estimate was 1,500, but he says the actual product will be greater than that amount. Is he correct? Explain how you know.

_____

_____

Name _____

Using Compatible Numbers to Estimate

Use compatible numbers to estimate 24 × 36.

Remember, compatible numbers are numbers that are easy to multiply.

Step 1	**Step 2**
Pick compatible numbers.	Multiply the compatible numbers.

Step 1
Pick compatible numbers.

• 24 is close to 25.

• 36 is close to 40.

24 × 36

25 × 40

Step 2
Multiply the compatible numbers.

25 × 40 = 1,000

So, 24 × 36 is about 1,000.

Estimate to find each product.

1. 23 × 12
23 is close to 25.

12 is close to _____.

25 × _____ = _____

2. 24 × 31
24 is close to 25.

31 is close to _____.

_____ × _____ = _____

3. 42 × 26
42 is close to _____.

26 is close to _____.

_____ × _____ = _____

4. 63 × 59
63 is close to _____.

59 is close to _____.

_____ × _____ = _____

5. 19 × 24 = _____

6. 51 × 17 = _____

7. 82 × 78 = _____

8. 24 × 61 = _____

9. 48 × 29 = _____

10. 53 × 39 = _____

11. There are 27 offices on each floor of a skyscraper. About how many offices are on 32 floors?

12. Yoko estimates that the product of 48 and 53 is 250. Is that reasonable? Why or why not?

_____

_____

Using Compatible Numbers to Estimate

Estimate to find each product.

1. 27 × 39 = _____   **2.** 27 × 22 = _____   **3.** 24 × 34 = _____

4. 78 × 21 = _____   **5.** 41 × 48 = _____   **6.** 23 × 28 = _____

7. 44 × 44 = _____   **8.** 72 × 38 = _____   **9.** 52 × 42 = _____

10. 67 × 18 = _____   **11.** 46 × 19 = _____   **12.** 34 × 48 = _____

13. **Number Sense** Marc estimates 67 × 36 by finding 70 × 40.
Will his estimate be greater or less than the actual product?
Explain how you know.

_____

_____

14. A total of 42 people can ride a Ferris wheel at one time.
What is the best way to estimate the number of people
that ride the Ferris wheel in 26 rides?

   A 40 × 20   **C** 40 × 25

   B 30 × 30   **D** 40 × 50

15. **Writing to Explain** Describe how you can use compatible numbers to
estimate 17 × 27.

_____

_____

Problem Solving: Multiple-Step Problems

Chad and Amy cut lawns in their neighborhood to make money. They charge $20 per lawn. One weekend, Amy cut 4 lawns, and Chad cut 3 lawns. How much money did they earn all together?

Solution One

Hidden Question: How many lawns did they mow all together?

Chad cut 3 lawns, Amy cut 4 lawns.

$$3 + 4 = 7$$

They cut 7 lawns.

Question in the Problem: How much money did they earn all together?

$$7 \text{ lawns} \times \$20 = \$140$$

Chad and Amy earned $140.

Solution Two

Hidden Question 1: How much money did Chad get for cutting lawns?

$$3 \times \$20 = \$60$$

Hidden Question 2: How much money did Amy get for cutting lawns?

$$4 \times \$20 = \$80$$

Question in the Problem: How much money did they earn all together?

$$\$60 + \$80 = \$140$$

Chad and Amy earned $140.

Write and answer the hidden question or questions. Then solve the problem. Write your answer in a complete sentence.

1. Keisha sold 8 ribbons and 6 pins at a craft fair. She sold the ribbons for $3 each and the pins for $2 each. How much money did Keisha earn?

   _____

   _____

   _____

   _____

2. Ken uses 6 apples and 2 bananas to make a fruit salad. He puts twice as many oranges as bananas in the salad. How many pieces of fruit will Ken use to make 2 fruit salads?

   _____

   _____

   _____

   _____

Problem Solving: Multiple-Step Problems

For Exercise **1**, write and answer the hidden question or questions. Then solve the problem. Write your answer in a complete sentence. Use the table at the right.

County Fair Admission	
Adults	$5
Students	$3
Children	$2

1. Mario and his family went to the county fair. They bought 2 adult passes and 3 children's passes. What was the total cost for the family?

   _____

   _____

   _____

   _____

2. A bus has 12 rows with 1 seat in each row on one side and 12 rows with 2 seats in each row on the other side. How many seats does the bus have in all?

   A 3 **B** 12 **C** 24 **D** 36

3. What hidden questions do you need to answer in Exercise **2**?

   _____

   _____

4. **Writing to Explain** Write a problem about going to the laundromat that has a hidden question. A single load of laundry costs $2 and a double load costs $4. Explain how you solved your problem.

   _____

   _____

   _____

Arrays and Multiplying 2-Digit Numbers

One way to find the product of 12 × 24 is by using an array.

Draw a rectangle 24 units long by 12 units wide.

Divide the rectangle by tens and ones for each factor.
Find the number of squares in each smaller rectangle. Then
add the numbers of squares in the four small rectangles.

$$
\begin{array}{r}
8 \\
40 \\
40 \\
+\ 200 \\
\hline
288
\end{array}
$$

So, 12 × 24 = 288.

Another way to find 12 × 24 is to
draw a table. Separate the factors
into tens and ones. Multiply to find
each product. Then add.

	20	4
10	200	40
2	40	8

8 + 40 + 40 + 200 = 288
So, 12 × 24 = 288.

Use the grid or table to find each product.

1. 11 × 22

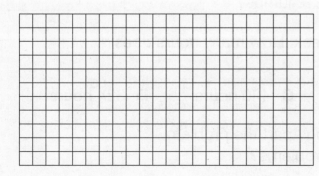

_____

2. 34 × 29

	20	9
30		
4		

_____

Name _____

Arrays and Multiplying 2-Digit Numbers

Use the grid to find each product.

1. 17 × 23

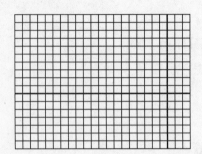

_____

2. 14 × 12

_____

Complete the table. Then find each product.

3. 31 × 19

	10	9
30		
1		

_____

4. 26 × 22

_____

5. 33 × 14

_____

6. 24 × 57 = _____

7. 44 × 48 = _____

8. A red kangaroo can cover 40 feet in 1 jump. How many feet can the red kangaroo cover in 12 jumps? _____

9. Barb exercises for 14 hours in 1 week. How many hours does she exercise in 32 weeks?

A 496 hours   **B** 448 hours   **C** 420 hours   **D** 324 hours

10. Writing to Explain How is breaking apart the problem 16 × 34 like solving four simpler problems?

_____

Name _____

Arrays and an Expanded Algorithm

You can use a place-value chart to organize the expanded algorithm to multiply.

Find 13 × 82.

Multiply the ones.					Multiply the tens.					Add the partial products.			
Th	**H**	**T**	**O**		**Th**	**H**	**T**	**O**		**Th**	**H**	**T**	**O**
		8	2				8	2				8	2
	×	1	**3**			×	**1**	3			×	1	3
	2	**4**	**6** **0**			2	4	6 0				2	4	6 0
						2	**0**	**0**			2	0	0
					8	**0**	**0**			+	8	0	0
										1	**0**	**6**	**6**

So, 13 × 82 = 1,066.

Solve.

1. A large assortment box has 64 crayons in it. The art teacher buys 24 large assortment boxes of crayons at the start of the school year. How many crayons is this in all?

_____

2. A new building will have 64 two-bedroom apartments. Each apartment will need 18 electrical outlets. How many outlets will the electricians have to install in all 64 apartments?

_____

3. **Number Sense** Use the place-value chart at the right to multiply 45 × 37. Be sure to record each partial product in the correct column of the chart. Beside each partial product, record the numbers you multiplied. Then find the final product.

Th	H	T	O	
		3	7	What I
	×	4	5	Multiply
				_____
				_____
				_____
+				_____

Name _____

Arrays and an Expanded Algorithm

Find each partial product. Then add to find the product.

1.
```
      29
  ×   47
```

2.
```
      91
  ×   64
```

3.
```
      38
  ×   48
```

Use the expanded algorithm to find the product.

4.
```
    79
  × 25
```

5.
```
    82
  × 14
```

6.
```
    53
  × 36
```

7.
```
    44
  × 31
```

8.
```
    35
  × 17
```

9.
```
    53
  × 28
```

10.
```
    41
  × 23
```

11.
```
    60
  × 16
```

12. Walter is a comic book artist. He usually draws 36 comic panels each day. How many comic panels can he draw in 2 weeks?

A 72 **B** 180 **C** 404 **D** 504

13. Writing to Explain Uma used the expanded algorithm to solve 62 × 13. Her work is shown at the right. What did she do wrong? Explain what partial products Uma should have added to find the correct product.

```
      13
  ×   62
       6
       2
     180
  +   60
     248
```

Name _____

Multiplying 2-Digit Numbers by Multiples of 10

Find the product of 60 and 26.

One way to find 60 × 26 is to use a grid.
Show 60 rows with 26 squares in each row.

Break apart 26 into tens and ones: 26 = 20 + 6.

Draw a vertical line on the grid to separate the
grid into two sections. Label one section 60 × 20.
Label the other section 60 × 6.

Multiply to find the partial products:
60 × 20 = 1,200 and 60 × 6 = 360.

Add the partial products:
1,200 + 360 = 1,560. So, 60 × 26 = 1,560.

A shorter way to find 60 × 26
is to multiply 6 tens × 26 by using
the standard algorithm.

$$\begin{array}{r} ^{3} \\ 26 \\ \times\ 60 \\ \hline 1,560 \end{array}$$

Record 0 in the ones place
of the product. Then find
6 tens × 26. The product is
156 tens or 1,560.

For Exercises **1** through **5**, find each product.

1. 23 × 40 _____

2. 16 × 30 _____

3. 34 × 50 _____

4. 60 × 47 _____

5. 17 × 80 _____

Name _____

Multiplying 2-Digit Numbers by Multiples of 10

Use the grid to find the partial products. Then add to find the total.

1. 23 × 50

_____

_____

2. 30 × 82

_____

_____

Find each product by using the standard algorithm.

3.   61
     ×   30
     ☐☐30

4.   32
     ×   60
     ☐☐20

5.   75
     ×   70
     ☐☐☐0

6.   93
     ×   50
     4☐☐☐

7.   66
     ×   20

8.   53
     ×   40

9.   86
     ×   80

10.   39
     ×   90

11. Which numbers are the partial products of 77 × 30?

A 210 and 700

B 2,100 and 210

C 511 and 2,100

D 4,900 and 210

12. Writing to Explain Explain how you can solve 40 × 16 by breaking apart the numbers.

_____

_____

Multiplying 2-Digit by 2-Digit Numbers

There are 24 cars in a race. Each car has 13 workers in the pit area. How many pit-area workers are at the race in all?

Step 1	Step 2	Step 3
Multiply the ones. Regroup if necessary.	Multiply the tens. Regroup if necessary.	Add the partial products.

Step 1:
```
  1
  24
× 13
────
  72  ← 3 × 24
```

Step 2:
```
  24
× 13
────
  72
 240  ← 10 × 24
```

Step 3:
```
   24
 × 13
─────
   72
 + 240
─────
  312
```

$24 \times 13 = 312$, so there are 312 pit-area workers at the race.

Find each product. Start multiplying the ones. Then multiply the tens.

1.
```
  38
× 26
```

2.
```
  67
× 27
```

3.
```
  47
× 85
```

4.
```
  88
× 32
```

5.
```
  53
× 48
```

6.
```
  18
× 77
```

7.
```
  67
× 34
```

8.
```
  91
× 46
```

9. **Reasonableness** Corina multiplied 62×22 and found a product of 1,042. Explain why Corina's answer is not reasonable.

_____

_____

_____

Multiplying 2-Digit by 2-Digit Numbers

Find the product.

1. 54 × 17	**2.** 36 × 20	**3.** 53 × 12	**4.** 48 × 46
5. 37 × 83	**6.** 62 × 17	**7.** 91 × 49	**8.** 28 × 56
9. 70 × 39	**10.** 58 × 90	**11.** 97 × 42	**12.** 64 × 88

13. A carton holds 24 bottles of juice. How many juice bottles are in 15 cartons?

_____

14. How much do 21 bushels of sweet corn weigh?

_____

15. How much do 18 bushels of asparagus weigh?

_____

Vegetable	Weight of 1 Bushel
Asparagus	24 pounds
Beets	52 pounds
Carrots	50 pounds
Sweet corn	35 pounds

16. How much more do 13 bushels of beets weigh than 13 bushels of carrots? _____

17. Which of the following is a reasonable answer for 92 × 98?

A 1,800 **B** 9,000 **C** 18,000 **D** 90,000

18. **Writing to Explain** Garth is multiplying 29 × 16. He found the partial product 174 after multiplying the ones and 290 after multiplying the tens. Explain how Garth can find the final product.

_____

Problem Solving:
Two-Question Problems

Read and Understand

Problem 1: Gina gave 3 sheets of paper to each of the 12 students in her class. How many sheets of paper did she give out?

Problem 2: Each sheet of paper had 3 paper clips attached to it. How many paper clips did she give out?

Answer Problem 1 first.

? sheets of paper											
3	3	3	3	3	3	3	3	3	3	3	3

12 students × 3 sheets of paper = 36 sheets of paper

Gina gave out 36 sheets of paper.

Plan and Solve

Use the answer from Problem 1 to solve Problem 2.

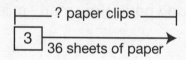

36 sheets of paper × 3 paper clips = 108 paper clips

Gina gave out 108 paper clips.

Solve. Use the answer from Problem 1 to solve Problem 2.

1. **Problem 1:** April made 16 baskets and glued 5 flowers on each one. How many flowers did she use in all?

   Problem 2: Each flower April used had 8 petals. How many petals were there on all the flowers she used?

2. **Problem 1:** Jorge washed cars for four hours on Saturday. In the first hour, he washed 4 cars. In the second hour, he washed 7 cars. In the third hour, he washed 9 cars. How many cars did he wash in the first three hours?

   Problem 2: Jorge washed the same number of cars in the fourth hour as he did in the first three hours combined. How many cars did he wash in all in four hours?

Problem Solving:
Two-Question Problems

For **1** and **2**, use the answer from the first problem to solve the second problem.

1. **Problem 1:** Francisco reads 75 pages every week for a summer reading program. If there are about 4 weeks in a month, then how many pages can Francisco read in a month?

_____

Problem 2: How many pages will Francisco read in the 3 months of summer?

_____

2. **Problem 1:** Mr. Dunn drives a 12-mile round trip 3 times a week to the dog park. How many miles does he drive?

_____

Problem 2: Mr. Dunn estimates he uses 4 gallons of gas over the course of the week to and from the dog park. How many miles per gallon does his car get?

_____

3. **Problem 1:** A company buys printer paper in a box that contains 8 packages. Which expression shows how many packages of paper are in 12 boxes?

   A $8 + 8$ **B** $8 \div 2$ **C** $8 + 12$ **D** 8×12

Problem 2: Each package of paper costs 3 dollars. Explain how to find how much 12 boxes of printer paper will cost.

_____

_____

_____

Name _____

Using Mental Math to Divide

When dividing numbers that end in zero, you can use basic division facts, as well as patterns, to help you divide mentally. For example:

	Find 210 ÷ 7.	Find 4,200 ÷ 6.
What You **Think**	First, find the basic fact. **210 ÷ 7 =** **21 ÷ 7 =** **21** tens ÷ **7 =** 3 tens or 30	Find the basic fact. **4,200 ÷ 6 =** **42 ÷ 6 =** **42** hundreds ÷ **6 =** 7 hundreds or 700
What You **Write**	210 ÷ 7 = 30	4,200 ÷ 6 = 700

Divide. Use mental math.

1. 250 ÷ 5 = _____

2. 7,200 ÷ 9 = _____

3. 200 ÷ 4 = _____

4. 2,800 ÷ 7 = _____

5. 810 ÷ 9 = _____

6. 5,000 ÷ 5 = _____

7. Number Sense What basic fact would you
use to help solve 4,500 ÷ 9? _____

8. In 1 week there are 7 days. How many weeks
are in 210 days? _____

9. How many weeks are there in 420 days? _____

Name _____

Using Mental Math to Divide

Divide. Use mental math.

1. 250 ÷ 5 = _____

2. 1,400 ÷ 2 = _____

3. 300 ÷ 5 = _____

4. 1,600 ÷ 4 = _____

5. 240 ÷ 8 = _____

6. 3,600 ÷ 4 = _____

7. 1,600 ÷ 2 = _____

8. 270 ÷ 3 = _____

9. 4,200 ÷ 7 = _____

10. 640 ÷ 8 = _____

11. 2,000 ÷ 5 = _____

12. 320 ÷ 8 = _____

13. 1,200 ÷ 2 = _____

14. 1,600 ÷ 8 = _____

The fourth grade performed a play based on the story of Cinderella. There was one chair for each person present.

15. On Friday, 140 people came to the play. The chairs in the auditorium were arranged in 7 equal rows. How many chairs were in each row? _____

16. There were 8 equal rows set up for Saturday's performance. There were 240 people at the play on Saturday. How many chairs were in each row? _____

17. Which is the quotient of 5,600 ÷ 8?

    A 40   **B** 400   **C** 70   **D** 700

18. **Writing to Explain** Explain why the following answer is not correct: 1,000 ÷ 5 = 2,000.

_____

_____

_____

Estimating Quotients

Estimate 460 ÷ 9.

You can use compatible numbers.

Ask yourself: What is a number close to 460 that could be easily divided by 9? Try 450.

450 ÷ 9 = 50

So, 460 ÷ 9 is about 50.

You can also estimate by thinking about multiplication.

Ask yourself: Nine times what number is about 460?

9 × 5 = 45, so 9 × 50 = 450.

So, 460 ÷ 9 is about 50.

50 is a good estimation for this problem.

Estimate each quotient.

1. 165 ÷ 4 _____

2. 35 ÷ 4 _____

3. 715 ÷ 9 _____

4. 490 ÷ 8 _____

5. 512 ÷ 5 _____

6. 652 ÷ 8 _____

7. 790 ÷ 9 _____

8. 200 ÷ 7 _____

9. 311 ÷ 6 _____

10. Number Sense Complete by filling in the circle with < or >. Without dividing, explain how you know which quotient is greater.
315 ÷ 5 ◯ 347 ÷ 5

_____

_____

Name _____

Estimating Quotients

Estimate each quotient.

1. 82 ÷ 4 _____

2. 580 ÷ 3 _____

3. 96 ÷ 5 _____

4. 811 ÷ 2 _____

5. 194 ÷ 6 _____

6. 207 ÷ 7 _____

7. 282 ÷ 4 _____

8. 479 ÷ 8 _____

9. Jacqui is writing a book. If she needs to write 87 pages in 9 days, about how many pages will she write each day? _____

10. Wade wants to give 412 of his marbles to 10 of his friends. If he gives each friend the same number of marbles, about how many will each friend receive? _____

11. Which is the best estimate for 502 ÷ 6?

A 60   **B** 70   **C** 80   **D** 90

12. Writing to Explain You are using division to determine how much whole wheat flour to use in a bread recipe. Is an estimated answer good enough?

_____

_____

Estimating Quotients for Greater Dividends

Find 294 ÷ 5.

Think of multiples of 5.   5, 10, 15, 20, 25, 30

Underline the first two digits of 2̲9̲4.

Find the multiple of 5 that is closest to 29. That multiple is 30.

$6 \times 5 = 30$, so
$60 \times 5 = 300$.
$300 \div 5 = 60$

294 ÷ 5 is about 60.

Estimate each quotient.

1. 1,561 ÷ 8

Think of multiples of 8.   8, 16, _____, _____, 40, _____

Underline the first two digits of 1,561.

Which multiple of 8 is closest to 15? _____

What is 200 × 8? _____

What is 1,600 ÷ 8? _____

So, 1,561 ÷ 8 is about _____.

2. 461 ÷ 9 _____

3. 2,356 ÷ 6 _____

4. 5,352 ÷ 9 _____

Name _____

Estimating Quotients for Greater Dividends

Estimate each quotient.

1. 381 ÷ 5 _____

2. 5,985 ÷ 9 _____

3. 2,753 ÷ 7 _____

4. 190 ÷ 8 _____

5. 427 ÷ 6 _____

6. 1,127 ÷ 4 _____

7. 143 ÷ 3 _____

8. 386 ÷ 9 _____

9. 4,088 ÷ 5 _____

10. 1,378 ÷ 4 _____

11. 4,405 ÷ 6 _____

12. 812 ÷ 7 _____

13. 3,942 ÷ 8 _____

14. 933 ÷ 3 _____

15. 4,471 ÷ 7 _____

16. 5,251 ÷ 9 _____

17. Daniel's family grows pecans. Last year they harvested
1,309 pounds of pecans. If they packed bags with
3 pounds of pecans in each bag, about how many
bags would they fill?

A 40 bags **B** 50 bags **C** 400 bags **D** 500 bags

18. Reason At Camp Summer Fun, 4 campers share each
tent. The camp is expecting 331 campers. About how
many tents will they need? Will the number of tents they
actually need be more or less than the estimate? How do
you know?

_____

_____

Dividing with Remainders

When you divide, you can think of putting items into groups.
For example:

$$60 \div 6 = 10$$

60 items   6 groups   10 items in
each group

Sometimes there are items left over. In division, the number of
"left over" items is called the **remainder**. For example:

$$62 \div 6 = 10 \text{ R2} \longrightarrow 2 \text{ items}$$
left over

62 items   6 groups   10 items in
each group

Divide. You may use counters or pictures to help.

1. $4\overline{)34}$ **2.** $8\overline{)65}$ **3.** $9\overline{)75}$

4. $6\overline{)27}$ **5.** $5\overline{)14}$ **6.** $9\overline{)37}$

7. Number Sense In division, why should the remainder not
be greater than the divisor?

_____

Dividing with Remainders

Divide. You may use counters or pictures to help.

1. 4)27 **2.** 6)32 **3.** 7)17 **4.** 9)29

5. 8)27 **6.** 3)27 **7.** 5)28 **8.** 4)35

9. 2)19 **10.** 7)30 **11.** 3)17 **12.** 9)16

If you arrange these items into equal rows, tell how many will be in each row and how many will be left over.

13. 26 shells into 3 rows _____

14. 19 pennies into 5 rows _____

15. 17 balloons into 7 rows _____

16. Reasonableness Ms. Nikkel wants to divide her class of 23 students into 4 equal teams. Is this reasonable? Why or why not?

_____

_____

17. Which is the remainder for the quotient of $79 \div 8$?

A 7 B 6 C 5 D 4

18. Writing to Explain Pencils are sold in packages of 5. Explain why you need 6 packages in order to have enough for 27 students.

_____

_____

Name _____

Multiplication and Division Stories

Multiply when you want to combine equal groups, and divide when you want to find the number of groups. You can draw a picture to help you interpret a story and turn it into a math problem.

A bicycle wheel has 36 spokes and spokes are sold in packages of 5. How many packages must you buy to replace all the spokes in a wheel?

You can draw a picture that shows the spokes in a package.

1. Do you want to combine equal groups or do you want to find the number of groups?

_____

2. Do you want to multiply or divide? _____

3. What is the number expression for this problem? _____

4. What is the solution to the expression? _____

5. How many packages must you buy? _____

6. **Writing to Explain** Why are the previous two answers different from each other?

_____

_____

Multiplication and Division Stories

Use the story to solve questions **1** through **4**.

1. 3 litters were born at Broadway Kennel last year, and each litter had 7 puppies. How many puppies were born at Broadway Kennel last year?

   _____

2. **Geometry** Martin is making squares by arranging 26 sticks. How many squares can he make? Write and solve the number fact you used to find the answer.

   _____

3. **Writing to Explain** 60 people will be attending a dinner party. Each table at the party can seat 8 people. How many tables are needed? Write and solve the number fact you used to find the answer, and explain your reasoning.

   _____

   _____

   _____

   _____

4. In a parking lot, some cars have 1 spare tire and others have no spare tires. All together, there are 43 tires and 9 cars. How many cars have a spare tire?

   _____

   _____

Write a multiplication story using the multiplication problem below. Then solve.

5. 14 × 4

   _____

   _____

   _____

Name _____

Problem Solving: Draw a Picture and Write an Equation

Read the question and follow the steps to solve.

Bryan has 24 bottles of water. He and his friends have 8 backpacks. If he puts the same number of bottles into each backpack, how many bottles will be in each?

Step 1: Read/Understand	**Step 2:** Plan and Solve	**Step 3:** Check
• Find the information the problem gives you. [There are 24 bottles of water and 8 backpacks.] • Find the information the problem wants you to figure out. [The number of bottles in each backpack]	• Draw a picture to help you visualize the problem. 24 in all ? | ? | ? | ? | ? | ? | ? | ? • Figure out which operation you need to use. [Division] • Write an equation. [24 ÷ 8 = ?] Solve. [? = 3 bottles]	$24 \div 8 = 3$ Check: $3 \times 8 = 24$ The answer checks.

1. **Strategy Practice** Joeli has 10 quarters. She wants to buy postcards to mail to her friends. Each postcard costs 2 quarters. How many postcards can she buy?

   • What does the question tell you?

   _____

   • What does the question ask you to find?

   _____

   • Write an equation. Solve and check.

   _____

   _____

Solve the following problems. Draw a picture to help.

2. Mack has 36 photos. His album can hold 9 photos per page. How many pages will he need to use? _____

3. There are 7 vans taking 56 students on a field trip. If each van has the same number of students, how many students are on each van? _____

Name _____

Problem Solving: Draw a Picture and Write an Equation

Solve. Draw a picture and write an equation to help you.

1. Terrence has 16 trophies and he wants to put an equal number on 4 shelves. How many trophies will he have on each shelf?

16 Trophies

| ? | ? | ? | ? |

↑Trophies per shelf

_____

2. Mrs. Parker has 21 bookmarks that she wants to give to her 7 reading club members. How many bookmarks will each member receive?

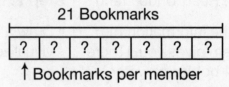

21 Bookmarks

| ? | ? | ? | ? | ? | ? | ? |

↑Bookmarks per member

_____

3. Lisa has 45 megabytes of space left on her flash drive. She has 5 files that are the same size that will fill up the space. How many megabytes is each file?

45 Megabytes

| ? | ? | ? | ? | ? |

↑Megabytes per file

_____

4. A store is displaying boxes of a new video game in 7 rows. If the store has 49 copies of the game, how many games are in each row?

49 Games

| ? | ? | ? | ? | ? | ? | ? |

↑Games in one row

_____

5. **Algebra** Remy is 8 years old. She is twice as old as her younger sister. Which expression below shows how old Remy's sister is?

A 8×2 **B** $8 \div 2$ **C** $8 + 2$ **D** $8 - 2$

6. Jillian wants to organize her CD collection into wooden crates. Each crate holds 8 CDs. Jillian has 48 CDs. How can she use a picture to figure out how many crates she needs?

_____

_____

_____

Using Objects to Divide: Division as Repeated Subtraction

When you divide, you subtract equal groups.

Doris has 32 strawberries. She makes box lunches by putting 4 strawberries in each box lunch. How many box lunches can she make this way?

What you think: Doris will put 4 strawberries in each lunch box. How many lunch boxes can she make?

What you show: Repeated subtraction

$32 - 4 = 28$	$16 - 4 = 12$
$28 - 4 = 24$	$12 - 4 = 8$
$24 - 4 = 20$	$8 - 4 = 4$
$20 - 4 = 16$	$4 - 4 = 0$

You can subtract 4 from 32 eight times.

What you write: $32 \div 4 = 8$

32 is the dividend, the number that is being divided.

4 is the divisor, the number the dividend is being divided by.

8 is the quotient, or the answer to the division problem.

Draw pictures to solve each problem.

1. You have 15 marbles. You put 5 marbles into each group. How many groups can you make?

   _____

2. You have 20 ice cubes. You put 4 ice cubes into each glass. How many glasses can you put ice cubes into?

   _____

Using Objects to Divide: Division as Repeated Subtraction

Draw pictures to solve each problem.

1. Anthony has 18 stickers. He wants to give 3 stickers to each of his friends. How many friends can he give stickers to?

_____

2. Mrs. Riggins has 40 glass tiles. She is going to put 8 glass tiles on each clay pot she is decorating. How many clay pots can she decorate this way?

_____

3. There are 21 students in Mr. Tentler's class. The class is being separated into groups of 3 students. How many groups can they form?

_____

4. Calvin reads a book that has 90 pages. If he reads 10 pages each day, how many days will it take him to finish reading the book?

    A 3 days

    B 6 days

    C 9 days

    D 12 days

5. A school district has 24 flags to give to schools. If it gives 4 flags to each school, how many schools can it give flags to? Explain your answer.

_____

_____

Division as Repeated Subtraction

For City Clean-Up Day, 18 people volunteered to clean up the city park. The volunteers worked in groups with 3 people each. How many groups of volunteers cleaned up the city park?

Use repeated subtraction to find the number of groups.

$18 - 3 = 15$
$15 - 3 = 12$
$12 - 3 = 9$
$9 - 3 = 6$
$6 - 3 = 3$
$3 - 3 = 0$

0   3   6   9   12 15 18

You subtract 3 six times.

There are 6 groups of volunteers.

Use repeated subtraction to divide. Use a number line to help.

0 1 2 3 4 5 6 7 8 9 10 11 12 13 14 15 16 17 18 19 20 21 22 23 24 25 26 27 28 29 30

1. Mark is placing 12 model cars into equal groups. Each group has 4 model cars. How many groups of model cars will he make?

_____

2. There are 24 students in gym class. They divided into teams of 6 for a volleyball game. How many teams were there?

_____

3. Each necklace Cara makes has 5 beads. How many necklaces can Cara make with 20 beads?

_____

4. Amy has 12 dolls in her collection. She places 6 dolls on each shelf. How many shelves does she need?

_____

5. Charlie has 16 chores to do. He can complete 4 chores in one day. How many days will Charlie take to complete his chores?

_____

6. The pet store has 9 parakeets. If 3 parakeets are in each cage, how many cages are there?

_____

7. Shawn needs to learn how to play 15 songs for his band's concert. If he learns 3 songs each week, how many weeks will it take him to learn all of the songs?

_____

8. At Rosa Elementary School, 27 teachers signed up to carpool. If 3 teachers ride together in each car, how many cars are needed for all of the teachers?

_____

Division as Repeated Subtraction

Use repeated subtraction to solve each problem. Draw pictures to help.

1. Roger buys a package of 16 rawhide bones for his dog. He gives his dog 4 bones each week. How many weeks will the package of rawhide bones last?

_____

2. During recess 24 students divided into kickball teams. Each team had 6 players. How many teams were there?

_____

3. Each member of a juggling troop juggles 6 balls at one time. The jugglers use 18 balls during a show. How many jugglers are in the show?

_____

4. The county fair has 4 people working at the snack bar each shift. If 32 people work at the snack bar each day, how many shifts are there?

_____

5. For a piano recital, Jessie is playing a song that is 3 minutes long. She practices by playing the song several times in a row. If she practices for 21 minutes, how many times does she play the song?

A 6   **B** 7   **C** 8   **D** 9

6. Ryan wants to prepare for a mini-marathon by jogging 12 miles each week. How many days would he need to jog if he runs only 3 miles each day? Explain.

_____

_____

Name _____

Using Objects to Divide: Division as Sharing

You can use models to help you solve division problems.
The models below help you find 78 ÷ 5.
Find 78 ÷ 5.
Estimate 80 ÷ 5 = 16.

First divide the tens.	Now, change the tens into the ones.	Now, divide the ones.	Now, write the remainder.

$$\begin{array}{r} 1 \\ 5\overline{)78} \\ -5 \end{array}$$ 5 tens

$$\begin{array}{r} 1 \\ 5\overline{)78} \\ -5 \\ \hline 28 \end{array}$$ 5 tens
28 ones

$$\begin{array}{r} 15 \\ 5\overline{)78} \\ -5 \\ \hline 28 \\ -25 \\ \hline 3 \end{array}$$ 5 tens
28 ones

$$\begin{array}{r} 15R3 \\ 5\overline{)78} \\ -5 \\ \hline 28 \\ -25 \\ \hline 3 \end{array}$$ 5 tens
28 ones

remainder

There is one tens block in each group of 5

2 tens blocks and 8 ones blocks are equal to 28 ones blocks

Each of the 5 groups has 1 tens block and 5 ones blocks

78 ÷ 5 = 15 R3

Use the models below to help you fill in the boxes.

1. 66 ÷ ☐ = ☐ R2

2. 97 ÷ 4 = ☐ R ☐

3. ☐ ÷ 7 = ☐ R6

4. 76 ÷ ☐ = ☐ R ☐

Name _____

Using Objects to Divide: Division as Sharing

Draw pictures to tell how many are in each group and how many are left over.

1. 57 CDs in 8 organizers

2. 62 stickers on 5 rolls

_____

3. 44 plants in 6 rows

4. 37 chairs for 9 tables

_____

In **5** through **8**, use the model to complete each division sentence.

5. 27 ÷ ☐ = ☐ R3

6. ☐ ÷ 9 = ☐

7. ☐ ÷ ☐ = ☐

8. ☐ ÷ ☐ = ☐ R☐

9. Ken has 72 marbles. He decides to share them with his friends so they can play a game. Which of the following models shows Ken sharing his marbles?

A

C

B

D

10. Writing to Explain At Mr. Horne's farm there are 53 cows. There are 4 people who milk the cows each day. Does each person milk the same number of cows? Use a model to help you.

_____

_____

Dividing 2-Digit by 1-Digit Numbers

You can find 2-digit quotients by breaking apart the problem and dividing tens, then ones.

Find 85 ÷ 5.
Estimate: 100 ÷ 5 = 20.

```
     17
  5)85
    -5
    35
   -35
     0
```

Check: 17 × 5 = 85.
The answer checks.

Find 55 ÷ 3.
Estimate: 60 ÷ 3 = 20.

```
     18 R1
  3)55
    -3
    25
   -24
     1
```

Check: 18 × 3 = 54.
54 + 1 = 55
The answer checks.

Find 83 ÷ 7.
Estimate: 84 ÷ 7 = 12.

```
     11 R6
  7)83
    -7
    13
    - 7
      6
```

Check: 11 × 7 = 77.
77 + 6 = 83
The answer checks.

Find the missing values.

1.

2.

3. 3)91

4. 4)86

5. 2)75

Name _____

Dividing 2-Digit by 1-Digit Numbers

1.

2.

3.

4. 2)72　　　**5.** 5)86　　　**6.** 7)94　　　**7.** 3)39

8. 8)99　　　**9.** 5)87　　　**10.** 2)96　　　**11.** 3)43

Mrs. Thomas is planning to provide snacks for 96 fourth graders when they go on a field trip to the aquarium. Each student will receive 1 of each snack. Using the bar graph to the right, how many packages of each snack does Mrs. Thomas need?

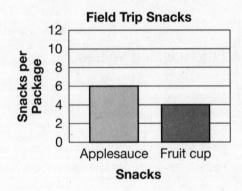

12. fruit cups _____

13. applesauce _____

14. Which is the remainder of 27 ÷ 4?

　　A 1　　　　　**B** 2　　　　　**C** 3　　　　　**D** 4

15. Writing to Explain Explain how to find the number of leftover pencils if Wendy wants to share 37 pencils with 9 people.

_____

_____

_____

Dividing 3-Digit by 1-Digit Numbers

You can find 3-digit quotients by breaking apart the problem.

Find 528 ÷ 4.	Find 575 ÷ 5.	Find 725 ÷ 3.
Estimate 500 ÷ 4 = 125.	Estimate 600 ÷ 5 = 120.	Estimate 750 ÷ 3 = 250.

$$
\begin{array}{r}
132 \\
4\overline{)528} \\
-\underline{4} \\
12 \\
-\underline{12} \\
8 \\
-\underline{8} \\
0
\end{array}
\qquad
\begin{array}{r}
115 \\
5\overline{)575} \\
-\underline{5} \\
7 \\
-\underline{5} \\
25 \\
-\underline{25} \\
0
\end{array}
\qquad
\begin{array}{r}
241 \text{ R2} \\
3\overline{)725} \\
-\underline{6} \\
12 \\
-\underline{12} \\
5 \\
-\underline{3} \\
2
\end{array}
$$

Check 132 × 4 = 528
The answer checks.

Check 115 × 5 = 575
The answer checks.

Check 241 × 3 = 723
723 + 2 = 725
The answer checks.

Find the missing values.

1.
$$
\begin{array}{r}
3\ 1\ 5\ \text{R}\ \boxed{} \\
2\overline{)6\ 3\ 1} \\
-\boxed{} \\
\boxed{} \\
-\ 2 \\
1\ 1 \\
-\ \boxed{}\ 0 \\
\boxed{}
\end{array}
$$

2.
$$
\begin{array}{r}
\boxed{}\boxed{}\boxed{}\ \text{R2} \\
6\overline{)7\ 8\ 8} \\
-\ 6 \\
1\ \boxed{} \\
-\ 1\ \boxed{} \\
\boxed{}\ 6 \\
-\ \boxed{}
\end{array}
$$

3. 3)462

4. 5)640

5. 9)919

Dividing 3-Digit by 1-Digit Numbers

In **1** through **8**, use place-value blocks to help you divide.

1. 4)412   **2.** 6)936   **3.** 7)798   **4.** 7)806

5. 3)420   **6.** 5)619   **7.** 7)842   **8.** 8)856

9. A train can hold 444 people in rows with 4 seats. How many 4-seat rows are there? _____

10. A song has 540 beats. If the song is 3 minutes long, how many beats per minute does the song have? _____

11. **Geometry** A circle has 360 degrees. If the circle is divided in half, how many degrees does each half measure? _____

12. Harvey has 513 stamps. He places an equal number in 3 stamp books. How many stamps are in each book? _____

13. Zeeshan has collected 812 autographs. Each autograph is either from a baseball star, a football star, a movie star, or a rock star. He has an equal number of autographs for each group. How many autographs does he have in each group? _____

14. Nicole has 369 tea bags. There are 3 different flavors of tea. What information do you need to find how many tea bags Nicole has of each flavor?

   A The number of flavors

   B The number of tea bags

   C If a tea bag can be divided into fourths

   D If there is an equal number of tea bags for each flavor

15. An ant has 6 legs. There are 870 legs in José's ant farm. How many ants are there in his ant farm?

   A 14 R5   **B** 145   **C** 864   **D** 5,220

16. **Writing to Explain** Jeff has 242 DVDs. He has 2 shelves that can each hold 120 DVDs. Does he need to buy another shelf?

Name _____

Deciding Where to Start Dividing

Sometimes there are not enough hundreds to divide by.
Sometimes you have to break up the hundreds into 10 tens.

Find $325 \div 5$.
Estimate $300 \div 5 = 60$.

Try to divide the hundreds.	Divide the tens.	Now divide the ones.
$5\overline{)325}$	$\begin{array}{r} 6 \\ 5\overline{)325} \\ -\underline{30} \quad \text{30 tens} \\ 2 \end{array}$	$\begin{array}{r} 65 \\ 5\overline{)325} \\ -\underline{30} \quad \text{30 tens} \\ 25 \\ -\underline{25} \quad \text{2 tens and} \\ 0 \quad \text{5 ones, no} \\ \text{remainder} \end{array}$

5 does not divide into 3. The 3 hundreds now have to be changed to 30 tens.

With 32 tens, 6 tens can go into each one of the 5 groups.

Each of the five groups has 6 tens and 5 ones.

Find the missing values in the problems below.

1.

2.

3. $5\overline{)125}$

4. $8\overline{)418}$

Deciding Where to Start Dividing

Complete each calculation.

1.

2.

3.

4.

5. 2)587

6. 8)747

7. Gerald distributes 582 brochures to 3 businesses each week. How many brochures does each business get?

A 159   **B** 174   **C** 194   **D** 264

8. Writing to Explain Write and solve a word problem for 456 ÷ 6.

_____

_____

_____

Dividing 4-Digit by 1-Digit Numbers

An estimate will help you decide where to place the first digit of the quotient. It will also help you check your answer.

Divide 5,493 ÷ 6.

Estimate first. You can use compatible numbers to divide mentally.	Divide to find the actual quotient.	Compare: Is the estimate close to the quotient?

54 is a multiple of 6.	☐☐☐ R☐
	6)5, 4 9 3
	−5 4
	  ☐☐
	− ☐
	  ☐☐
	− ☐☐
	    ☐
		estimate: _____

5,400 is close to 5,493 and 5,400 ÷ 6 will be easy to divide.		quotient: _____
5,400 ÷ 6 = _____		If it is, then your answer is reasonable.

Estimate. Then find each quotient. Use your estimate to check if your quotient is reasonable.

1. Divide 4,318 ÷ 7.

Estimate:

_____ ÷ _____ = _____

4,318 ÷ 7 = _____

Is your answer reasonable? _____

2. Divide 4,826 ÷ 5.

Estimate:

_____ ÷ _____ = _____

4,826 ÷ 5 = _____

Is your answer reasonable? _____

3. Divide 4,377 ÷ 8.

Estimate:

_____ ÷ _____ = _____

4,377 ÷ 8 = _____

Is your answer reasonable? _____

4. Divide 7,192 ÷ 9.

Estimate:

_____ ÷ _____ = _____

7,192 ÷ 9 = _____

Is your answer reasonable? _____

Dividing 4-Digit by 1-Digit Numbers

Estimate. Then find each quotient. Use your estimate to check if your answer is reasonable.

1. $4\overline{)1{,}227}$

2. $5\overline{)2{,}438}$

3. $8\overline{)4{,}904}$

4. $7\overline{)2{,}611}$

5. $6\overline{)4{,}998}$

6. $9\overline{)3{,}834}$

7. $3\overline{)1{,}675}$

8. $4\overline{)1{,}254}$

9. $544 \div 8 =$ _____

10. $2{,}430 \div 6 =$ _____

11. At the airport, there are 1,160 seats in the waiting areas. There are 8 separate, same size, waiting areas. How many seats are in each waiting area? _____

12. A wall by the school parking lot has an area of 1,666 square feet. Seven teams of students will paint a mural on the wall. Each team will paint an equal area of the wall. How many square feet will each team paint? _____

13. **Geometry** Conner put a fence around the perimeter of his rectangular yard. The perimeter of the yard is 858 feet. Conner put a fence post in every 6 feet. How many fence posts did he use?

A 142 R4   **B** 143   **C** 143 R2   **D** 153

14. Lilly estimated a quotient of 120 and found an actual quotient of 83. What should she do next? Explain.

_____

_____

_____

_____

Problem Solving: Multiple-Step Problems

Solve Problems Step-by-Step

Scott and Gina want to go see a movie after they eat dinner. They have brought $35 with them. Scott's meal costs $9 and Gina's meal costs $8. Movie tickets are $9 each. Will they have enough money left over after dinner to pay for 2 movie tickets?

First Step
Write down what you know:
- They have $35 to spend.
- They are spending $9 and $8 on dinner.

Second Step
Write down what you need to know:
- How much money is left over?
- Is it enough for 2 movie tickets?

Third Step
Develop a problem-solving strategy:
- Subtract $9 and $8 from $35.
  (Tip: Instead of subtracting these from $35 one at a time, combine them and then subtract from $35.)

$$\begin{array}{r} \$\ 9 \\ +\$\ 8 \\ \hline \$17.00 \end{array} \quad \text{then,} \quad \begin{array}{r} \$35 \\ -\$17 \\ \hline \$18 \end{array}$$

Fourth Step
Finish the problem:
- Is $18 enough for 2 movie tickets that cost $9 each?
  $9 \times 2 = $18
  They have $18 left. Yes, they have enough for 2 movie tickets.

Solve the problems below using the step-by-step process.

1. Nick and his friends are working on a project. They need to write 29 pages altogether. If his friend Kara writes 14 pages, and his friend Jared writes 12 pages, how many pages are left for Nick to write? _____

2. Ashlyn and Brooke went to the arcade with $18. They bought 4 bottles of water, which cost $2 each. They each bought a sticker book for $3 each. Ashlyn put $1 in a fundraiser jar. A game of pool cost $3 per game. Did they have enough money left to play? _____

3. **Reasoning** Cyndi and Jewel went shopping for school supplies. They had $14 to spend. They spent $4 on pencils, $3 on pens, and $6 on notebook paper. Cyndi thought she had enough money left over to buy a $2 pencil sharpener. Was she correct?

Problem Solving:
Multiple-Step Problems

Write and answer the hidden question or questions.
Then solve the problem. Write your answer in a
complete sentence.

County Fair Admission	
Adults	$5
Students	$3
Children	$2

1. Mario and his family went to the county
   fair. They bought 2 adult passes and
   3 children's passes. What was the
   total cost for the family?

   _____

   _____

   _____

2. A bus has 12 rows with 1 seat in each row on one side and
   12 rows with 2 seats in each row on the other side. How
   many seats does the bus have altogether?

   _____

   _____

   _____

3. **Writing to Explain** Write a problem about going to the laundromat
   that has a hidden question. A single load of laundry costs $2 and a
   double load costs $4. Solve your problem.

   _____

   _____

   _____

Factors

When multiplying two numbers, you know that both numbers are factors of the product.

Example 1

Find the factors of 24.

Factors   Product

$1 \times 24 = 24$
$2 \times 12 = 24$
$3 \times 8 = 24$
$4 \times 6 = 24$

Factors of 24:
1, 2, 3, 4, 6, 8, 12, and 24

Example 2

Find the factors of 16.

What two numbers multiply together to equal 16?

$1 \times 16 = 16$
$2 \times 8 = 16$
$4 \times 4 = 16$
$8 \times 2 = 16$
$16 \times 1 = 16$

Factors of 16: 1, 2, 4, 8, and 16

List all the factors of each number.

1. 18

2. 21

3. 11

4. 14

5. 23

6. 33

7. Number Sense Irene wants to list all of the factors for the number 42. She writes 2, 3, 6, 7, 14, 21, and 42. Is she correct? Explain.

_____

_____

_____

_____

Name _____

Factors

For **1** through **12**, find all the factors of each number.

1. 54

_____

_____

2. 17

_____

_____

3. 28

_____

_____

4. 31

_____

_____

5. 44

_____

_____

6. 47

_____

_____

7. 77

_____

_____

8. 71

_____

_____

9. 65

_____

_____

10. 23

_____

_____

11. 57

_____

_____

12. 24

_____

_____

13. Karl's mother buys 60 party favors to give out as gifts during Karl's birthday party. Which number of guests will NOT let her divide the party favors evenly among the guests?

A 12   **B** 15   **C** 20   **D** 25

14. Writing to Explain Mrs. Fisher has 91 watches on display at her store. She says she can arrange them into rows and columns without any watches left over. Mr. Fisher says that she can only make 1 row with all 91 watches. Who is right and why?

_____

_____

_____

Prime and Composite Numbers

A **composite number** is a whole number greater than 1 that has more than two different factors. 15 has four different factors, 1, 3, 5, and 15, so 15 is a composite number.

A **prime number** is a whole number greater than 1 that has exactly two factors, itself and 1. 17 has exactly two factors, 1 and 17, so 17 is a prime number.

Example 1	Example 2
Is 7 a prime or composite number?	Is 6 a prime or composite number?
Find all the factors of 7.	Find all the factors of 6.
Factors of 7: 1, 7	Factors of 6: 1, 2, 3, 6
1 and 7 divide evenly into 7.	1, 2, 3, and 6 divide evenly into 6.
7 is a prime number because it only has two factors, the number itself and 1.	6 is a composite number because it has more than two factors.

Tell if the number is prime or composite.

1. 5

2. 12

3. 18

_____

4. 15

5. 37

6. 43

_____

Prime and Composite Numbers

In **1** through **16**, write whether each number is prime or composite.

1. 81

2. 43

3. 572

4. 63

_____

_____

_____

_____

5. 53

6. 87

7. 3

8. 27

_____

_____

_____

_____

9. 88

10. 19

11. 69

12. 79

_____

_____

_____

_____

13. 3,235

14. 1,212

15. 57

16. 17

_____

_____

_____

_____

17. Mr. Gerry's class has 19 students, Ms. Vernon's class has 21 students, and Mr. Singh's class has 23 students. Whose class has a composite number of students?

_____

18. Every prime number greater than 10 has a digit in the ones place that is included in which set of numbers below?

A 1, 3, 7, 9

C 0, 2, 4, 5, 6, 8

B 1, 3, 5, 9

D 1, 3, 7

19. Writing to Explain Marla says that every number in the nineties is composite. Jackie says that one number in the nineties is prime. Who is correct? Explain your answer.

_____

_____

_____

Multiples

You can use a multiplication table to help find some multiples for numbers.

What are some multiples of 5?

Step 1 Find the column for 5.

Step 2 All the numbers in that column are multiples of 5.

Tip You could use the row for 5 instead of the column for 5.

In the chart, the multiples of 5 are 5, 10, 15, 20, 25, 30, 35, 40, and 45.

×	1	2	3	4	5	6	7	8	9
1	1	2	3	4	⑤	6	7	8	9
2	2	4	6	8	10	12	14	16	18
3	3	6	9	12	15	18	21	24	27
4	4	8	12	16	20	24	28	32	36
5	5	10	15	20	25	30	35	40	45
6	6	12	18	24	30	36	42	48	54
7	7	14	21	28	35	42	49	56	63
8	8	16	24	32	40	48	56	64	72
9	9	18	27	36	45	54	63	72	81

In **1** through **8**, write five multiples of each number.

1. 3

2. 7

3. 9

4. 2

_____   _____   _____   _____

5. 1

6. 8

7. 6

8. 4

_____   _____   _____   _____

In **9** through **12**, tell whether the first number is a multiple of the second number.

9. 18, 3

10. 24, 6

11. 32, 7

12. 12, 4

_____   _____   _____   _____

13. Number Sense What number has 12, 24, and 30 as multiples? Explain how you found your answer.

_____

_____

_____

Name _____

Multiples

In **1** through **8**, write five multiples of each number.

1. 5   **2.** 3   **3.** 7   **4.** 4

_____   _____   _____   _____

5. 9   **6.** 2   **7.** 6   **8.** 8

_____   _____   _____   _____

In **9** through **16**, tell whether the first number is a multiple of the second number.

9. 21, 7   **10.** 28, 3   **11.** 17, 3   **12.** 20, 4

_____   _____   _____   _____

13. 54, 9   **14.** 15, 5   **15.** 26, 4   **16.** 32, 8

_____   _____   _____   _____

17. Circle the number in the box that is a multiple of 8.

10	18	20	24	31	36

18. **Number Sense** List five multiples for 3 and five multiples for 4. Then circle the common multiples.

_____

_____

19. **Reasoning** What number has factors of 2 and 3 and multiples of 12 and 18?

_____

20. What are five multiples of 9?

   A 9, 19, 29, 39, 49   **B** 9, 18, 27, 36, 45   **C** 1, 3, 9, 18, 27   **D** 1, 9, 18, 27, 36

21. Carmen listed the multiples of 6 as 1, 2, 3, and 6.
Is she correct? Explain why or why not.

_____

_____

Equivalent Fractions

If two fractions name the same amount, they are called **equivalent fractions**.

Use multiplication to write a fraction equivalent to $\frac{1}{2}$.

Multiply the numerator and denominator by the same number.

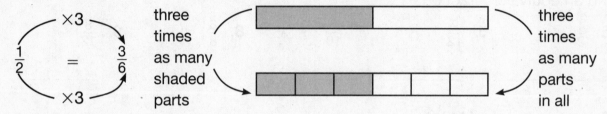

$\times 3$

$\frac{1}{2} = \frac{3}{6}$

$\times 3$

three times as many shaded parts

three times as many parts in all

$\frac{1}{2}$ and $\frac{3}{6}$ are equivalent fractions.

Use division to write a fraction that is equivalent to $\frac{10}{12}$.

Think of a number that is a factor of both 10 and 12. Two is a factor of 10 and 12. Divide the numerator and the denominator by 2.

$\div 2$

$\frac{10}{12} = \frac{5}{6}$ $\frac{10}{12}$ and $\frac{5}{6}$ are equivalent fractions.

$\div 2$

Find the missing number.

1. $\frac{1}{4} = \frac{\square}{8}$ ____

2. $\frac{9}{12} = \frac{\square}{4}$ ____

3. $\frac{2}{3} = \frac{\square}{6}$ ____

4. $\frac{4}{5} = \frac{\square}{10}$ ____

Multiply to find an equivalent fraction.

5. $\frac{1}{4} =$ ____

6. $\frac{1}{2} =$ ____

7. $\frac{1}{6} =$ ____

8. $\frac{3}{4} =$ ____

Divide to find an equivalent fraction.

9. $\frac{8}{12} =$ ____

10. $\frac{9}{12} =$ ____

11. $\frac{4}{8} =$ ____

12. $\frac{2}{6} =$ ____

13. $\frac{4}{10} =$ ____

14. $\frac{5}{10} =$ ____

15. $\frac{8}{10} =$ ____

16. $\frac{6}{8} =$ ____

Equivalent Fractions

Find the missing number.

1. $\frac{1}{2} = \frac{\square}{12}$

2. $\frac{6}{10} = \frac{\square}{5}$

3. $\frac{3}{12} = \frac{\square}{4}$

4. $\frac{4}{5} = \frac{\square}{10}$

_____   _____   _____   _____

Find an equivalent fraction.

5. $\frac{1}{2}$

6. $\frac{2}{12}$

7. $\frac{6}{10}$

8. $\frac{6}{8}$

9. $\frac{8}{12}$

_____   _____   _____   _____   _____

10. Is $\frac{2}{14}$ equivalent to $\frac{3}{7}$? _____

11. In Mark's collection of antique bottles, $\frac{1}{2}$ of the bottles
    are dark green. Write three equivalent fractions for $\frac{1}{2}$.

_____

12. Write a pair of equivalent fractions for the picture below.

_____

13. At the air show, $\frac{1}{3}$ of the airplanes were gliders.
    Which fraction is an equivalent fraction for $\frac{1}{3}$?

    A $\frac{4}{6}$ **B** $\frac{2}{12}$ **C** $\frac{4}{12}$ **D** $\frac{3}{6}$

14. In Missy's sports-card collection, $\frac{3}{4}$ of the cards are baseball
    cards. In Frank's collection, $\frac{8}{12}$ are baseball cards. Frank says
    they have the same fraction of baseball cards. Is he correct?

_____

_____

Number Lines and Equivalent Fractions

Write two equivalent fractions that name the point on the number line.

0   1

Step 1 Count the number of tick marks from 0 to 1.	**Step 2** Count the number of tick marks from 0 to where the point is.	**Step 3** 12 is an even number, so it can be divided by 2.
On this number line, there are 12. That tells you the denominator of one fraction is 12.	There are 8. That tells you the numerator of the fraction is 8. You now know one fraction that names the point is $\frac{8}{12}$.	$12 \div 2 = 6$

Step 3 continued:

If you count every second tick mark from 0 to 1, you will count 6 tick marks. The denominator of another fraction is 6.

Now, count every second tick mark from 0 to the location of the point. There are 4, so the numerator of the fraction is 4. An equivalent fraction to $\frac{8}{12}$ is $\frac{4}{6}$.

$$\frac{8}{12} = \frac{4}{6}$$

Write two fractions that name the point on the number line.

1.

0   1

_____

2.

0   1

_____

3. Draw a Diagram Are $\frac{3}{8}$ and $\frac{3}{4}$ equivalent fractions? Draw a number line to show your answer.

_____

_____

_____

Name _____

Number Lines and Equivalent Fractions

Write two fractions that name each point on the number line.

1. _____

2. _____

3. _____

4. _____

5. Draw a number line to show that $\frac{2}{3}$ and $\frac{4}{6}$ are equivalent.

6. Draw a number line to show that $\frac{3}{5}$ and $\frac{6}{10}$ are equivalent.

7. Which of the following pairs are **NOT** equivalent fractions?

  A $\frac{1}{3}, \frac{5}{8}$ **B** $\frac{2}{4}, \frac{4}{8}$ **C** $\frac{3}{5}, \frac{6}{10}$ **D** $\frac{3}{4}, \frac{9}{12}$

8. **Writing to Explain** How many fractions are equivalent to $\frac{4}{5}$? Explain.

_____

_____

_____

_____

Comparing Fractions

Leanne wanted to compare $\frac{4}{6}$ and $\frac{3}{4}$. She used fraction strips to help.

				$\frac{1}{6}$	$\frac{1}{6}$	$\frac{4}{6}$
					$\frac{1}{4}$	$\frac{3}{4}$

She compared the amounts that were shaded in each picture. Because the amount shaded in $\frac{3}{4}$ is more than the amount shaded in $\frac{4}{6}$, she knew that $\frac{3}{4}$ is greater than $\frac{4}{6}$.

So, $\frac{3}{4} > \frac{4}{6}$.

Write $>$ or $<$ for each $\bigcirc$. Use fraction strips or benchmark fractions to help.

1. $\frac{5}{6}\bigcirc\frac{2}{3}$

2. $\frac{1}{5}\bigcirc\frac{2}{8}$

3. $\frac{9}{10}\bigcirc\frac{6}{8}$

4. $\frac{3}{4}\bigcirc\frac{1}{4}$

5. $\frac{7}{8}\bigcirc\frac{5}{10}$

6. $\frac{2}{5}\bigcirc\frac{2}{6}$

7. $\frac{1}{3}\bigcirc\frac{3}{8}$

8. $\frac{2}{10}\bigcirc\frac{3}{5}$

The same number of students attended school all week.

Day	Fraction of students buying lunch
Monday	$\frac{1}{2}$
Tuesday	$\frac{2}{5}$
Wednesday	$\frac{3}{4}$
Thursday	$\frac{5}{8}$
Friday	$\frac{4}{6}$

9. Did more students buy lunch on Tuesday or on Wednesday? _____

10. Did more students buy lunch on Thursday or on Friday? _____

Name _____

Comparing Fractions

Write > or < for each $\bigcirc$. You may use fraction strips to help.

1. $\frac{1}{2}$ $\bigcirc$ $\frac{3}{10}$ **2.** $\frac{8}{12}$ $\bigcirc$ $\frac{5}{12}$ **3.** $\frac{3}{8}$ $\bigcirc$ $\frac{1}{2}$

4. $\frac{3}{3}$ $\bigcirc$ $\frac{7}{8}$ **5.** $\frac{3}{5}$ $\bigcirc$ $\frac{1}{3}$ **6.** $\frac{1}{4}$ $\bigcirc$ $\frac{2}{4}$

7. $\frac{5}{6}$ $\bigcirc$ $\frac{5}{8}$ **8.** $\frac{7}{12}$ $\bigcirc$ $\frac{4}{5}$ **9.** $\frac{3}{10}$ $\bigcirc$ $\frac{6}{10}$

10. **Number Sense** Explain how you know that $\frac{21}{30}$ is greater than $\frac{2}{3}$.

_____

_____

_____

11. Tina completed $\frac{2}{3}$ of her homework.
George completed $\frac{7}{8}$ of his homework.
Who completed a greater fraction of homework? _____

12. Jackson played a video game for $\frac{1}{6}$ hour. Hailey played
a video game for $\frac{1}{3}$ hour. Who played the video game
for a greater amount of time? _____

13. Which fraction is greater than $\frac{3}{4}$?

A $\frac{1}{2}$ **B** $\frac{2}{5}$ **C** $\frac{5}{8}$ **D** $\frac{7}{8}$

14. **Writing to Explain** James says that $\frac{5}{5}$ is greater than $\frac{9}{10}$.
Is he correct? Explain.

_____

_____

_____

Ordering Fractions

How can you order fractions?

Order $\frac{2}{3}$, $\frac{1}{6}$, $\frac{7}{12}$ from least to greatest.

$\frac{1}{3}$			$\frac{1}{3}$			$\frac{1}{3}$		
$\frac{1}{6}$		$\frac{1}{6}$	$\frac{1}{6}$		$\frac{1}{6}$	$\frac{1}{6}$		$\frac{1}{6}$
$\frac{1}{12}$	$\frac{1}{12}$	$\frac{1}{12}$	$\frac{1}{12}$	$\frac{1}{12}$	$\frac{1}{12}$	$\frac{1}{12}$	$\frac{1}{12}$	$\frac{1}{12}$	$\frac{1}{12}$	$\frac{1}{12}$	$\frac{1}{12}$

Find equivalent fractions with a common denominator.

$\frac{1}{12}$	$\frac{1}{12}$	$\frac{1}{12}$	$\frac{1}{12}$	$\frac{1}{12}$	$\frac{1}{12}$	$\frac{1}{12}$	$\frac{1}{12}$

$\frac{1}{12}$	$\frac{1}{12}$

$\frac{1}{12}$	$\frac{1}{12}$	$\frac{1}{12}$	$\frac{1}{12}$	$\frac{1}{12}$	$\frac{1}{12}$	$\frac{1}{12}$

Compare the numerators.
Order the fractions from least to greatest.
$\frac{2}{12} < \frac{7}{12} < \frac{8}{12}$.

Order the fractions from least to greatest.

1. $\frac{3}{10}$, $\frac{3}{6}$, $\frac{2}{5}$

$\frac{1}{10}$	$\frac{1}{10}$	$\frac{1}{10}$
$\frac{1}{5}$		$\frac{1}{5}$
$\frac{1}{6}$	$\frac{1}{6}$	$\frac{1}{6}$

2. $\frac{3}{8}$, $\frac{1}{3}$, $\frac{3}{12}$

Find equivalent fractions with a common denominator and order from least to greatest.

3. $\frac{1}{2}$, $\frac{3}{4}$, $\frac{4}{6}$ _____

4. $\frac{3}{4}$, $\frac{2}{3}$, $\frac{7}{8}$ _____

5. $\frac{3}{10}$, $\frac{1}{2}$, $\frac{4}{5}$ _____

6. $\frac{1}{2}$, $\frac{3}{10}$, $\frac{3}{5}$ _____

7. $\frac{2}{3}$, $\frac{5}{6}$, $\frac{1}{2}$ _____

8. $\frac{5}{8}$, $\frac{3}{4}$, $\frac{3}{8}$ _____

Ordering Fractions

Order the fractions from least to greatest.

1. $\frac{3}{5}, \frac{7}{8}, \frac{5}{6}$

2. $\frac{1}{2}, \frac{7}{12}, \frac{4}{10}$

3. $\frac{2}{6}, \frac{1}{4}, \frac{5}{12}$

4. $\frac{3}{10}, \frac{2}{5}, \frac{1}{3}$

Find equivalent fractions with a common denominator and order from least to greatest.

5. $\frac{2}{3}, \frac{1}{2}, \frac{5}{12}$ _____

6. $\frac{1}{6}, \frac{1}{3}, \frac{3}{4}$ _____

7. $\frac{5}{6}, \frac{2}{3}, \frac{3}{4}$ _____

8. $\frac{7}{12}, \frac{2}{6}, \frac{1}{4}$ _____

9. $\frac{4}{5}, \frac{3}{10}, \frac{1}{2}$ _____

10. $\frac{9}{12}, \frac{1}{3}, \frac{3}{6}$ _____

11. Which fraction is greater than $\frac{2}{3}$?

A $\frac{1}{12}$ **B** $\frac{2}{6}$ **C** $\frac{5}{12}$ **D** $\frac{6}{8}$

12. Writing to Explain Explain how you know that $\frac{7}{12}$ is greater than $\frac{1}{3}$ but less than $\frac{2}{3}$?

_____

_____

_____

_____

Problem Solving: Writing to Explain

Gina and her brother Don made homemade pasta with their mother. Gina made $\frac{1}{4}$ of a pan of pasta. Don made $\frac{3}{8}$ of a pan. Which person made more pasta?

Writing to Explain

- Write your explanation in steps to make it clear.

- Tell what the numbers mean in your explanation.

- Tell why you took certain steps.

Example

- Because $\frac{1}{4}$ and $\frac{3}{8}$ have different denominators, I multiplied the numerator and denominator of $\frac{1}{4}$ by 2 to get $\frac{2}{8}$.

- Then I could compare the numerators of $\frac{2}{8}$ and $\frac{3}{8}$. Because $\frac{3}{8}$ is greater than $\frac{2}{8}$ I knew that Don made more pasta.

1. Rick has a collection of 6 video games. He lets his best friend borrow $\frac{2}{6}$ of his video game collection. Write two fractions equivalent to this number. Explain how you came up with the fractions.

_____

_____

_____

_____

_____

_____

Problem Solving:
Writing to Explain

1. Mary has 12 marbles. $\frac{3}{12}$ of the marbles are yellow and $\frac{2}{12}$ of the marbles are blue. The rest of the marbles are green. How many marbles are green? Explain how you know.

_____

_____

_____

_____

2. Adam wants to compare the fractions $\frac{3}{12}$, $\frac{1}{6}$, and $\frac{1}{3}$. He wants to order them from least to greatest and rewrite them so they all have the same denominator. Explain how Adam can rewrite the fractions.

_____

_____

_____

_____

3. Adam used the three fractions to make a circle graph and colored each a different color. What fraction of the graph is not colored? Explain your answer.

_____

_____

_____

Name _____

Modeling Addition of Fractions

Eight friends want to see a movie. Four of them want to see a comedy. Two want to see an action movie and two want to see a science-fiction movie. What fraction of the group wants to see either a comedy or a science-fiction movie?

You can use a model to add fractions.

Look at the circle. It is divided into eighths, because there are eight people in the group. Each person represents $\frac{1}{8}$ of the group. Four people want to see a comedy. Shade in four of the sections to represent $\frac{4}{8}$. Two people want to see a science-fiction movie. Shade in two more sections to represent $\frac{2}{8}$. Count the number of shaded sections. There are six. So, $\frac{6}{8}$ of the group wants to see either a comedy or a science fiction movie.

$\frac{4}{8} + \frac{2}{8} = \frac{6}{8}$ Write the sum in simplest form. $\frac{6 \div 2}{8 \div 2} = \frac{3}{4}$

Find each sum. Simplify, if possible.

1. $\frac{2}{5} + \frac{1}{5}$ _____

2. $\frac{4}{6} + \frac{1}{6}$ _____

3. $\frac{3}{8} + \frac{3}{8}$ _____

4. $\frac{1}{6} + \frac{1}{6}$ _____

5. $\frac{2}{5} + \frac{3}{5}$ _____

6. $\frac{2}{10} + \frac{3}{10}$ _____

7. $\frac{5}{8} + \frac{3}{8}$ _____

8. $\frac{3}{10} + \frac{1}{10}$ _____

9. $\frac{3}{4} + \frac{1}{4}$ _____

10. $\frac{5}{10} + \frac{4}{10}$ _____

11. $\frac{1}{6} + \frac{1}{6} + \frac{1}{6}$ _____

12. $\frac{1}{12} + \frac{5}{12} + \frac{2}{12}$ _____

13. **Number Sense** We can express time as a fraction of an hour. For example, 15 minutes is $\frac{1}{4}$ hour. 30 minutes is $\frac{1}{2}$ hour. What fraction of an hour is 45 minutes? _____

R 12·1

Modeling Addition of Fractions

Find each sum. Simplify if possible. You may use fraction strips.

1. $\frac{1}{4} + \frac{1}{4}$ _____

2. $\frac{2}{5} + \frac{1}{5}$ _____

3. $\frac{3}{12} + \frac{1}{12}$ _____

4. $\frac{2}{6} + \frac{3}{6}$ _____

5. $\frac{1}{2} + \frac{2}{2}$ _____

6. $\frac{2}{8} + \frac{5}{8}$ _____

7. $\frac{3}{8} + \frac{3}{8}$ _____

8. $\frac{3}{10} + \frac{2}{10}$ _____

9. $\frac{1}{6} + \frac{2}{6}$ _____

10. Draw a Picture A rectangular garden is divided into 10 equal parts. Draw a picture that shows $\frac{3}{10} + \frac{3}{10} = \frac{6}{10}$, or $\frac{3}{5}$.

11. Each day, Steven walked $\frac{1}{12}$ mile more than the previous day. The first day he walked $\frac{1}{12}$, the second day he walked $\frac{2}{12}$ mile, the third day he walked $\frac{3}{12}$ mile. On which day did the sum of his walks total at least 1 complete mile?

_____

12. Algebra Find the missing value in the equation.

$\frac{3}{12} + \frac{1}{12} + \frac{?}{12} = \frac{1}{2}$

A 1　　　　　**B** 2　　　　　**C** 3　　　　　**D** 4

13. There are five people sitting around the dinner table. Each person has $\frac{2}{10}$ of a pie on their plate. How much pie is left? Explain.

_____

_____

_____

Adding Fractions with Like Denominators

When you add fractions with like denominators, add the numerators and keep the denominator the same.

Find the sum of $\frac{3}{8} + \frac{1}{8}$

Add the numerators. $3 + 1 = 4$

Keep the denominator the same. $\frac{3}{8} + \frac{1}{8} = \frac{4}{8}$

Is this fraction expressed in simplest form?

Remember: a fraction is in simplest form when the greatest common factor (GCF) of the numerator and denominator is 1.

$\frac{4 \div 4}{8 \div 4} = \frac{1}{2}$ $\frac{1}{2}$ is in simplest form, because the GCF of 1 and 2 is 1.

Find each sum. Simplify if possible.

1. $\frac{1}{3} + \frac{1}{3}$ _____

2. $\frac{3}{10} + \frac{6}{10}$ _____

3. $\frac{5}{12} + \frac{2}{12}$ _____

4. $\frac{3}{12} + \frac{7}{12}$ _____

5. $\frac{5}{10} + \frac{3}{10}$ _____

6. $\frac{2}{8} + \frac{4}{8}$ _____

7. $\frac{7}{10} + \frac{3}{10}$ _____

8. $\frac{1}{8} + \frac{6}{8}$ _____

9. $\frac{1}{10} + \frac{5}{10}$ _____

10. $\frac{1}{5} + \frac{2}{5} + \frac{2}{5}$ _____

11. $\frac{2}{8} + \frac{1}{8} + \frac{4}{8}$ _____

12. $\frac{2}{6} + \frac{1}{6}$ _____

13. Reasoning There were 10 bowling pins standing before Jared took his first turn. On his first turn, he knocked down 5 pins. On his second turn, he knocked down 3 pins. What fraction of the pins did Jared knock down in his two turns? _____

Name _____

Adding Fractions with Like Denominators

Find each sum. Simplify if possible.

1. $\frac{2}{5} + \frac{2}{5}$ _____

2. $\frac{4}{10} + \frac{5}{10}$ _____

3. $\frac{3}{8} + \frac{1}{8}$ _____

4. $\frac{3}{6} + \frac{2}{6}$ _____

5. $\frac{2}{10} + \frac{7}{10}$ _____

6. $\frac{5}{8} + \frac{2}{8}$ _____

7. $\frac{1}{6} + \frac{2}{6}$ _____

8. $\frac{9}{12} + \frac{2}{12}$ _____

9. $\frac{4}{12} + \frac{6}{12}$ _____

10. $\frac{2}{12} + \frac{9}{12}$ _____

11. $\frac{1}{8} + \frac{3}{8} + \frac{2}{8}$ _____

12. $\frac{2}{10} + \frac{1}{10} + \frac{5}{10}$ _____

13. $\frac{4}{12} + \frac{2}{12} + \frac{1}{12}$ _____

14. $\frac{2}{5} + \frac{1}{5} + \frac{1}{5}$ _____

15. **Geometry** A side of an equilateral triangle is $\frac{2}{8}$ cm long. Draw a picture that shows the triangle. What is the perimeter of the triangle? _____

16. Of the computer games Lynne owns, $\frac{5}{12}$ are sport games and $\frac{3}{12}$ are educational. What fraction of the games are either sport games or educational games?

    A $\frac{4}{12}$ **B** $\frac{1}{2}$ **C** $\frac{2}{3}$ **D** $\frac{3}{4}$

17. Rob and Nancy are working on a project. Rob completes $\frac{1}{8}$ of it on Monday and $\frac{3}{8}$ of it on Tuesday. Nancy completes $\frac{2}{8}$ of it on Wednesday and $\frac{1}{8}$ of it on Thursday. Is the project complete? Explain.

_____

_____

Modeling Subtraction of Fractions

Karla made a pizza and cut it into 10 slices. She ate two slices. What fraction of the pizza is left?

You can use a model to subtract fractions.

Karla's pizza is divided into 10 slices. One way to show this is $\frac{10}{10} = 1$ whole pizza. Karla ate two slices of the pizza. Cross out two of the slices. Count the number of slices left. There are 8 slices or $\frac{8}{10}$ of the pizza left.

$$\frac{10}{10} - \frac{2}{10} = \frac{8}{10}$$

Write the answer in simplest form, if possible.

$$\frac{8 \div 2}{10 \div 2} = \frac{4}{5}$$

Use fraction strips or models to subtract. Simplify if possible.

1. $\frac{5}{5} - \frac{2}{5} =$ _____   **2.** $\frac{7}{10} - \frac{3}{10} =$ _____   **3.** $\frac{3}{4} - \frac{2}{4} =$ _____

4. $\frac{8}{10} - \frac{5}{10} =$ _____   **5.** $\frac{6}{6} - \frac{3}{6} =$ _____   **6.** $\frac{11}{12} - \frac{7}{12} =$ _____

7. $\frac{5}{6} - \frac{2}{6} =$ _____   **8.** $\frac{4}{8} - \frac{2}{8} =$ _____   **9.** $\frac{11}{12} - \frac{8}{12} =$ _____

10. $\frac{7}{12} - \frac{5}{12} =$ _____   **11.** $\frac{6}{10} - \frac{4}{10} =$ _____   **12.** $\frac{9}{12} - \frac{6}{12} =$ _____

13. Algebra Find x.

$$x - \frac{1}{6} = \frac{1}{6}$$ _____

Modeling Subtraction
of Fractions

Use fraction strips to subtract. Simplify if possible.

1. $\frac{11}{12} - \frac{5}{12}$ _____

2. $\frac{6}{12} - \frac{4}{12}$ _____

3. $\frac{1}{2} - \frac{1}{2}$ _____

4. $\frac{4}{6} - \frac{1}{6}$ _____

5. $\frac{5}{6} - \frac{4}{6}$ _____

6. $\frac{9}{10} - \frac{3}{10}$ _____

7. $\frac{5}{8} - \frac{2}{8}$ _____

8. $\frac{7}{8} - \frac{5}{8}$ _____

9. $\frac{3}{4} - \frac{2}{4}$ _____

10. $\frac{3}{5} - \frac{2}{5}$ _____

11. $\frac{2}{5} - \frac{1}{5}$ _____

12. $\frac{9}{12} - \frac{1}{12}$ _____

13. **Algebra** Evaluate $\frac{5}{8} - ? = \frac{3}{8}$. _____

14. **Draw a Diagram** Harriet has $\frac{3}{4}$ tank of gas left in her car.
    If she needs $\frac{1}{4}$ tank to go to her friend's house and another
    $\frac{1}{4}$ tank to get back home, does she have enough gas?
    Draw a diagram and explain your answer.

    _____

    _____

15. Alicia had $\frac{10}{12}$ yard of fabric. She used $\frac{8}{12}$ for a pillow. How much
    fabric did she have left? Explain how you found your answer.

    _____

    _____

Subtracting Fractions with Like Denominators

When subtracting with two fractions having the same denominator, the difference also has the same denominator.

Find $\frac{7}{8} - \frac{5}{8}$.

Step 1:	**Step 2:**	**Step 3:**
Subtract the numerators.	Write the difference over the same denominator.	Simplify the answer if possible.
$7 - 5 = 2$	$\frac{7}{8} - \frac{5}{8} = \frac{2}{8}$	$\frac{2}{8} = \frac{1}{4}$

So, $\frac{7}{8} - \frac{5}{8} = \frac{1}{4}$.

Subtract the fractions. Simplify if possible.

1. $\frac{4}{5} - \frac{3}{5}$ _____

2. $\frac{8}{12} - \frac{3}{12}$ _____

3. $\frac{3}{6} - \frac{1}{6}$ _____

4. $\frac{9}{10} - \frac{3}{10}$ _____

5. $\frac{11}{12} - \frac{5}{12}$ _____

6. $\frac{5}{6} - \frac{1}{6}$ _____

7. $\frac{97}{100} - \frac{40}{100}$ _____

8. $\frac{5}{8} - \frac{1}{8}$ _____

9. $\frac{7}{10} - \frac{2}{10} - \frac{1}{10}$ _____

10. $\frac{7}{12} - \frac{4}{12}$ _____

11. $\frac{3}{4} - \frac{1}{4} - \frac{2}{4}$ _____

12. $\frac{8}{8} - \frac{1}{8}$ _____

13. **Reasoning** During archery practice, Manny hit the target 7 times out of 10 tries. What fraction of his arrows did NOT hit the target?

_____

Name _____

Subtracting Fractions with Like Denominators

In **1** through **12**, find each difference. Simplify if possible.

1. $\frac{4}{5} - \frac{1}{5}$ _____

2. $\frac{9}{10} - \frac{5}{10}$ _____

3. $\frac{5}{8} - \frac{2}{8}$ _____

4. $\frac{6}{8} - \frac{2}{8}$ _____

5. $\frac{9}{10} - \frac{8}{10}$ _____

6. $\frac{9}{12} - \frac{5}{12}$ _____

7. $\frac{5}{6} - \frac{3}{6}$ _____

8. $\frac{3}{4} - \frac{1}{4}$ _____

9. $\frac{6}{8} - \frac{4}{8}$ _____

10. $\frac{7}{12} - \frac{3}{12}$ _____

11. $\frac{10}{12} - \frac{6}{12}$ _____

12. $\frac{4}{6} - \frac{4}{6}$ _____

13. **Geometry** The area of rectangle A is $\frac{11}{12}$ square meters. The area of rectangle B is $\frac{8}{12}$ square meters. How much larger is rectangle A?

_____

14. Joan counted that $\frac{2}{10}$ of her jelly beans were red. Dean counted that $\frac{6}{10}$ of his jelly beans were red. How much greater a fraction of Dean's jelly beans were red?

_____

15. **Think About the Process** On the weekends, Paul jogs $\frac{9}{10}$ mile. On the weekdays, Paul jogs $\frac{5}{10}$ mile. Which expression shows how many more miles Paul jogs on the weekends than on a weekday?

    A $\frac{9}{10} + \frac{5}{10}$ **B** $\frac{9}{10} - \frac{5}{10}$ **C** $\frac{5}{10} + \frac{9}{10}$ **D** $\frac{5}{10} - \frac{9}{10}$

16. In a classroom, $\frac{2}{12}$ of the students play baseball, $\frac{4}{12}$ play football, $\frac{1}{12}$ are in the chorus, and the rest participate in volunteer programs. What fraction of the students participate in volunteer programs? Explain your answer.

_____

_____

_____

Adding and Subtracting on the Number Line

Bernadette has $\frac{7}{8}$ yard of ribbon. She cuts off $\frac{3}{8}$ yard to make a collar for her dog. How much ribbon does Bernadette have left?

You can use a number line to help you subtract fractions.

Draw a number line to represent the ribbon. Divide the number line into eighths. Place a point at $\frac{7}{8}$ to show the length of the ribbon before it is cut. Draw an arrow $\frac{3}{8}$ of a unit to the left to show how much of the ribbon Bernadette cut off.

$\frac{7}{8} - \frac{3}{8} = \frac{4}{8}$ Simplify: $\frac{4}{8} = \frac{1}{2}$ There is $\frac{1}{2}$ yard of ribbon left.

You can also use a number line to help you add fractions.

Kevin and Duane are recycling aluminum cans. Each boy has collected $\frac{4}{10}$ pound. How many pounds have they collected in all?

Divide this number line into tenths. Start at zero and draw an arrow to and place a point at $\frac{4}{10}$ to show the amount of aluminum Kevin collected. Now draw another arrow $\frac{4}{10}$ of a unit long to the right to show Duane's amount.

$\frac{4}{10} + \frac{4}{10} = \frac{8}{10}$ Simplify: $\frac{8}{10} = \frac{4}{5}$ The boys collected $\frac{4}{5}$ pound of aluminum.

Add or subtract the fractions. You may use a number line. Simplify your answer, if possible.

1. $\frac{2}{5} + \frac{1}{5} =$ _____

2. $\frac{8}{12} - \frac{3}{12} =$ _____

3. $\frac{5}{10} - \frac{3}{10} =$ _____

4. $\frac{2}{6} + \frac{1}{6} =$ _____

5. $\frac{29}{100} - \frac{4}{100} =$ _____

6. $\frac{1}{8} + \frac{2}{8} + \frac{3}{8} =$ _____

Adding and Subtracting on the Number Line

Write the equation shown by each number line.
Write your answer. Simplify if possible.

1.

_____

2.

_____

Draw a number line to solve. Simplify if possible.

3. $\frac{3}{8} + \frac{2}{8}$ _____

4. $\frac{9}{12} - \frac{3}{12}$ _____

5. Draw a Diagram Ann is growing two different plants for a science project. Plant A grew $\frac{4}{12}$ inch the first week and $\frac{2}{12}$ inch the second week. Plant B grew $\frac{7}{12}$ inch the first week and did not grow after that. Show the heights of each plant on a different number line. Which plant is taller now?

_____

6. Which equation is represented by the number line below?

```
      ⌢⌢⌢⌢⌢⌢⌢
   ←┼──┼──┼──┼──┼──→
    0  1  2  3  1
       4  4  4
```

A $\frac{1}{4} + \frac{2}{4} = \frac{3}{4}$ **B** $\frac{1}{4} + \frac{3}{4} = \frac{4}{4}$ **C** $\frac{1}{4} + \frac{1}{4} = \frac{2}{4}$ **D** $\frac{1}{3} + \frac{1}{3} = \frac{2}{3}$

7. Dave made fruit punch for his party but accidentally tripped and spilled $\frac{5}{12}$ of the punch. How much of the punch was left? Explain how you found your answer.

_____

Improper Fractions and Mixed Numbers

You can use fraction strips to write a mixed number as an improper fraction.

$3\frac{1}{2}$ of the model below is shaded.

$\frac{1}{2}$	$\frac{1}{2}$
$\frac{1}{2}$	$\frac{1}{2}$
$\frac{1}{2}$	$\frac{1}{2}$
$\frac{1}{2}$	$\frac{1}{2}$

Into how many parts is each strip divided? 2. This is your denominator.

Count the shaded halves. There are 7. This is your numerator.

$3\frac{1}{2}$ is the same as the improper fraction $\frac{7}{2}$.

You can also use fraction strips to write an improper fraction as a mixed number.

$\frac{8}{3}$ of the model below is shaded.

$\frac{1}{3}$	$\frac{1}{3}$	$\frac{1}{3}$
$\frac{1}{3}$	$\frac{1}{3}$	$\frac{1}{3}$
$\frac{1}{3}$	$\frac{1}{3}$	$\frac{1}{3}$

How many strips are completely shaded? 2. This is your whole number.

What fraction of the third strip is shaded? $\frac{2}{3}$. This is your fraction.

$\frac{8}{3}$ is the same as the mixed number $2\frac{2}{3}$.

Write each mixed number as an improper fraction.

1. $2\frac{1}{3}$ _____

2. $4\frac{1}{5}$ _____

3. $2\frac{3}{4}$ _____

4. $5\frac{2}{6}$ _____

Write each improper fraction as a mixed number or a whole number.

5. $\frac{13}{12}$ _____

6. $\frac{50}{10}$ _____

7. $\frac{23}{10}$ _____

8. $\frac{17}{8}$ _____

9. Writing to Explain Is $\frac{45}{5}$ equal to a whole number or a mixed number? Explain how you know.

_____

_____

_____

_____

Improper Fractions and Mixed Numbers

Write each mixed number as an improper fraction.

1. $3\frac{2}{5}$ _____

2. $6\frac{1}{4}$ _____

3. $2\frac{1}{12}$ _____

4. $2\frac{7}{10}$ _____

Write each improper fraction as a mixed number or whole number.

5. $\frac{12}{5}$ _____

6. $\frac{24}{3}$ _____

7. $\frac{32}{3}$ _____

8. $\frac{20}{12}$ _____

9. **Number Sense** Matt had to write $3\frac{4}{12}$ as an improper fraction. Write how you would tell Matt the easiest way to do so.

_____

_____

_____

_____

10. Jill has $\frac{11}{8}$ ounces of trail mix. Write the weight of Jill's trail mix as a mixed number. _____

11. Nick had $1\frac{3}{4}$ gal of milk. Write the amount of milk Nick has as an improper fraction. _____

12. Which is **NOT** an improper fraction equal to 8?

   A $\frac{24}{3}$ B $\frac{42}{6}$ C $\frac{32}{4}$ D $\frac{64}{8}$

13. **Writing to Explain** Write three different improper fractions that equal $4\frac{1}{2}$. (Hint: find equivalent fractions.)

_____

_____

Modeling Addition and Subtraction of Mixed Numbers

Example 1: Draw a model to add $1\frac{7}{8} + 2\frac{3}{8}$.

Step 1 Model each mixed number using fraction strips.

Step 2 Add the fractions. Regroup if you can.

$$\frac{7}{8}$$
$$+\frac{3}{8}$$
$$\frac{10}{8} = 1\frac{2}{8}$$

Step 3 Add the whole numbers to the regrouped fractions. Write the sum. Simplify, if possible.

So, $1\frac{7}{8} + 2\frac{3}{8} = 4\frac{1}{4}$.

Example 2: Draw a model to subtract $2\frac{1}{5} - 1\frac{2}{5}$.

Step 1 Model the number you are subtracting from, $2\frac{1}{5}$.

Step 2 Rename $2\frac{1}{5}$ as $1\frac{6}{5}$. Cross out one whole and $\frac{2}{5}$ to show subtracting $1\frac{2}{5}$.

Express the part of the model that is not crossed out as a fraction or mixed number. So, $2\frac{1}{5} - 1\frac{2}{5} = \frac{4}{5}$.

Use fraction strips to find each sum or difference. Simplify, if possible.

1. $3\frac{1}{2} + 1\frac{1}{2}$ **2.** $2\frac{5}{8} + 4\frac{3}{8}$ **3.** $5\frac{2}{6} + 3\frac{5}{6}$ **4.** $2\frac{2}{4} + 6\frac{3}{4}$

5. $6\frac{1}{8} - 3\frac{5}{8}$ **6.** $8\frac{3}{12} - 2\frac{5}{12}$ **7.** $12\frac{1}{3} - 5\frac{2}{3}$ **8.** $9\frac{7}{10} - 6\frac{9}{10}$

Modeling Addition and Subtraction of Mixed Numbers

For **1** and **2**, use each model to find each sum or difference.

1. $1\frac{3}{8} + 1\frac{7}{8}$

2. $3\frac{1}{5} - 1\frac{4}{5}$

Use fraction strips to find each sum or difference.
Simplify, if possible.

3. $2\frac{1}{3} + 1\frac{2}{3}$

4. $3\frac{5}{6} + 4\frac{3}{6}$

5. $5\frac{1}{4} - 1\frac{2}{4}$

6. $12\frac{3}{8} - 2\frac{5}{8}$

7. $8\frac{1}{6} - 3\frac{5}{6}$

8. $4\frac{6}{10} + 5\frac{7}{10}$

9. $7\frac{1}{3} - 4\frac{2}{3}$

10. $6\frac{2}{5} + 3\frac{4}{5}$

11. $1\frac{1}{6} + 3\frac{5}{6}$

12. $2\frac{4}{8} + 6\frac{7}{8}$

13. $6\frac{3}{5} - 4\frac{3}{5}$

14. $5\frac{1}{3} - 4\frac{2}{3}$

15. Jerome's rain gauge showed $13\frac{9}{10}$ centimeters (cm) at the end of last month. At the end of this month, the rain gauge showed $15\frac{3}{10}$ centimeters. How many more centimeters of rain fell this month?

A $29\frac{2}{10}$ cm

B $15\frac{3}{10}$ cm

C $2\frac{4}{10}$ cm

D $1\frac{4}{10}$ cm

16. You are adding $3\frac{2}{3} + 2\frac{2}{3}$ using fraction strips. Explain how you rename the fraction part of the problem.

_____

_____

Adding Mixed Numbers

Randy talks on the telephone for $2\frac{5}{6}$ hours, and then surfs the Internet for $3\frac{3}{4}$ hours. How many hours does he spend on the two activities?

Step 1. Write equivalent fractions with the least common denominator. You can use fraction strips to show the equivalent fractions.

$$3\frac{3}{4} = 3\frac{9}{12}$$

$$2\frac{5}{6} = 2\frac{10}{12}$$

Step 2. Add the fraction part of the mixed number first. Then add the whole numbers.

$$\frac{9}{12} + \frac{10}{12} = \frac{19}{12} \qquad 3 + 2 = 5$$

$$\frac{19}{12} + 5 = 5\frac{19}{12}$$

Step 3. Simplify the sum if possible.

$$5\frac{19}{12} = 6\frac{7}{12} \text{ hours}$$

So, $2\frac{5}{6} + 3\frac{3}{4} = 6\frac{7}{12}$.

In **1** through **6**, find each sum. Simplify if possible.

1. $2\frac{10}{12}$
    $+ 3\frac{3}{12}$
    _____

2. $1\frac{3}{8}$
    $+ 6\frac{6}{8}$
    _____

3. $5\frac{4}{10}$
    $+ 4\frac{2}{10}$
    _____

4. $10\frac{2}{6} + \frac{3}{6} =$ _____

5. $3\frac{3}{12} + 6\frac{8}{12} =$ _____

6. $1\frac{2}{5} + 3\frac{1}{5} =$ _____

7. **Geometry** Tirzah wants to put a fence around her garden. She has 22 yards of fence material. Does she have enough to go all the way around the garden?

Tirzah's garden $4\frac{8}{12}$ yards

$6\frac{9}{12}$ yards

_____

_____

_____

Name _____

Adding Mixed Numbers

In **1** through **6**, find each sum. Simplify, if possible. Estimate for reasonableness.

1. $7\frac{2}{6} + 8\frac{5}{6}$ _____

2. $4\frac{3}{4} + 2\frac{2}{4}$ _____

3. $11\frac{9}{10} + 3\frac{2}{10}$ _____

4. $7\frac{9}{8} + 5\frac{2}{8}$ _____

5. $5\frac{8}{12} + 3\frac{5}{12}$ _____

6. $21\frac{11}{12} + 17\frac{5}{12}$ _____

7. **Number Sense** Write two mixed numbers that have a sum of 3.

_____

8. What is the total measure of an average man's brain and heart in kilograms (kg)?

_____

Vital Organ Measures

Average woman's brain	$1\frac{3}{10}$ kg	$2\frac{8}{10}$ lb
Average man's brain	$1\frac{4}{10}$ kg	3 lb
Average human heart	$\frac{3}{10}$ kg	$\frac{7}{10}$ lb

9. What is the total weight of an average woman's brain and heart in pounds (lb)? _____

10. What is the sum of the measures of an average man's brain and an average woman's brain in kilograms? _____

11. Which is a good comparison of the estimated sum and the actual sum of $7\frac{9}{12} + 2\frac{11}{12}$?

   A Estimated < actual   **C** Actual > estimated

   B Actual = estimated   **D** Estimated > actual

12. Can the sum of two mixed numbers be equal to 2? Explain why or why not.

_____

_____

_____

Name _____

Subtracting Mixed Numbers

The Plainville Zoo has had elephants for $12\frac{4}{6}$ years. The zoo has had zebras for $5\frac{3}{6}$ years. How many years longer has the zoo had elephants?

Step 1: Write equivalent fractions with the least common denominator. You can use fraction strips.

$12\frac{4}{6}$

$5\frac{3}{6}$

Step 2: Find the difference of $12\frac{4}{6} - 5\frac{3}{6}$. Subtract the fractions. Then subtract the whole numbers. Simplify the difference if possible.

$\frac{4}{6} - \frac{3}{6} = \frac{1}{6}$ $12 - 5 = 7$

So, $12\frac{4}{6} - 5\frac{3}{6} = 7\frac{1}{6}$ years.

Example 2: Sometimes you may have to rename a fraction so you can subtract. Find the difference of $6 - 2\frac{3}{8}$.

$$6 \longrightarrow \text{rename} \longrightarrow 5\frac{8}{8}$$
$$-2\frac{3}{8} \qquad\qquad\qquad -2\frac{3}{8}$$
$$\overline{} \qquad\qquad\qquad \overline{3\frac{5}{8}}$$

For **1** through **4**, find each difference. Simplify, if possible.
Remember: You may have to rename a fraction in order to subtract.

1. $4\frac{5}{8}$
      $-2\frac{2}{8}$
      _____

2. $5\frac{7}{12}$
      $-1\frac{2}{12}$
      _____

3. 3
      $-1\frac{3}{4}$
      _____

4. $6\frac{5}{6}$
      $-5\frac{4}{6}$
      _____

5. **Number Sense** To find the difference of $7 - 3\frac{5}{12}$, how do you rename the 7?

_____

6. Robyn ran $5\frac{3}{4}$ miles last week. She ran $4\frac{1}{4}$ miles this week. How many more miles did she run last week?

_____

R 12•9

Name _____

Subtracting Mixed Numbers

For **1** through **10**, find each difference. Simplify, if possible.

1. $10\frac{3}{4}$
$-7\frac{1}{4}$

2. $7\frac{4}{6}$
$-2\frac{3}{6}$

3. 3
$-2\frac{2}{3}$

4. $17\frac{8}{12}$
$-12\frac{3}{12}$

5. $9\frac{2}{6} - 6\frac{5}{6}$ _____

6. $4\frac{1}{5} - 2\frac{3}{5}$ _____

7. $6\frac{3}{12} - 3\frac{4}{12}$ _____

8. $5\frac{2}{8} - 3\frac{7}{8}$ _____

9. $8\frac{1}{4} - 7\frac{3}{4}$ _____

10. $2\frac{9}{10} - 2\frac{5}{10}$ _____

Strategy Practice The table shows the length and width of several kinds of bird eggs.

11. How much longer is the Canada goose egg than the raven egg?

_____

12. How much wider is the turtledove egg than the robin egg?

_____

Egg Sizes in Inches (in.)

Bird	Length	Width
Canada goose	$3\frac{4}{10}$	$2\frac{3}{10}$
Robin	$\frac{8}{10}$	$\frac{6}{10}$
Turtledove	$1\frac{2}{10}$	$\frac{9}{10}$
Raven	$1\frac{9}{10}$	$1\frac{3}{10}$

13. Which is the difference of $21\frac{1}{4} - 18\frac{2}{4}$?

A $2\frac{1}{4}$ **B** $2\frac{2}{4}$ **C** $2\frac{3}{4}$ **D** $3\frac{1}{4}$

14. Explain why it is necessary to rename $4\frac{1}{4}$ if you subtract $\frac{3}{4}$ from it.

_____

_____

_____

Decomposing and Composing Fractions

Example 1

$$\begin{array}{r} \frac{1}{9} \\ + \frac{2}{9} \\ \hline \end{array}$$

The denominators are the same, so you can add the numerators.

$\frac{3}{9} = \frac{1}{3}$ Rewrite $\frac{3}{9}$ as $\frac{1}{3}$

Example 2

$\frac{1}{8} + \frac{3}{8} + \frac{5}{8} = \frac{9}{8}$ or $1\frac{1}{8}$

Show another way to make this sum.

$\frac{6}{8} + \frac{3}{8} = \frac{9}{8} = 1\frac{1}{8}$

Add or subtract fractions and write answers in simplest form. For the addition problems, write another addition problem that has the same sum and uses two or more fractions.

1. $\frac{1}{4} + \frac{1}{4}$ **2.** $\frac{2}{3} - \frac{1}{3}$ **3.** $\frac{2}{8} + \frac{5}{8}$ **4.** $\frac{5}{6} - \frac{1}{6}$ **5.** $\frac{4}{12} + \frac{2}{12}$

_____ _____ _____ _____ _____

6. $\begin{array}{r} \frac{5}{6} \\ - \frac{2}{6} \\ \hline \end{array}$ **7.** $\begin{array}{r} \frac{3}{10} \\ + \frac{3}{10} \\ \hline \end{array}$ **8.** $\begin{array}{r} \frac{9}{10} \\ - \frac{3}{10} \\ \hline \end{array}$ **9.** $\begin{array}{r} \frac{3}{12} \\ + \frac{6}{12} \\ \hline \end{array}$ **10.** $\begin{array}{r} \frac{44}{100} \\ - \frac{24}{100} \\ \hline \end{array}$

11. At lunch, Alice ate $\frac{3}{8}$ of her sandwich. Later, for a snack, she ate another $\frac{3}{8}$ of the sandwich. Write an addition sentence that shows how much of the sandwich Alice ate. Suppose Alice ate the same total amount of her sandwich at 3 different times instead of 2. Write an addition problem that shows the amount she ate as a sum of 3 fractions.

_____

_____

Decomposing and Composing Fractions

For **1** through **15**, add or subtract the fractions. For the addition problems, write another addition problem that has the same sum and uses two or more fractions.

1. $\frac{1}{8} + \frac{3}{8} =$ _____

2. $\frac{8}{10} + \frac{1}{10} =$ _____

3. $\frac{1}{3} + \frac{1}{3} =$ _____

4. $\begin{array}{r} \frac{3}{8} \\ + \frac{3}{8} \\ \hline \end{array}$

5. $\begin{array}{r} \frac{1}{5} \\ + \frac{2}{5} \\ \hline \end{array}$

6. $\begin{array}{r} \frac{3}{6} \\ + \frac{2}{6} \\ \hline \end{array}$

7. $\frac{9}{12} - \frac{2}{12} =$ _____

8. $\frac{4}{8} - \frac{2}{8} =$ _____

9. $\frac{6}{10} - \frac{1}{10} =$ _____

10. $\begin{array}{r} \frac{5}{8} \\ - \frac{2}{8} \\ \hline \end{array}$

11. $\begin{array}{r} \frac{7}{10} \\ - \frac{1}{10} \\ \hline \end{array}$

12. $\begin{array}{r} \frac{8}{10} \\ - \frac{4}{10} \\ \hline \end{array}$

13. $\begin{array}{r} \frac{1}{6} \\ + \frac{2}{6} \\ \hline \end{array}$

14. $\begin{array}{r} \frac{1}{3} \\ + \frac{1}{3} \\ \hline \end{array}$

15. $\begin{array}{r} \frac{1}{4} \\ + \frac{1}{4} \\ \hline \end{array}$

16. Jacob is making a stew. The stew calls for $\frac{3}{8}$ cup of rice. If he triples the recipe, how much rice will he need? Write an addition problem to show your answer.

_____

17. Which of the following fractions is not an equivalent fraction to $\frac{1}{2}$?

A $\frac{3}{6}$ **B** $\frac{4}{8}$ **C** $\frac{6}{10}$ **D** $\frac{6}{12}$

18. **Writing to Explain** Gerry folded $\frac{3}{8}$ of the pile of shirts. Molly folded $\frac{1}{8}$ of the pile of shirts. Together, did they fold more than half the shirts? Explain your answer.

_____

Problem Solving: Draw a Picture and Write an Equation

Read and Understand   Pippa filled $\frac{1}{8}$ of a jar with blue stones, $\frac{2}{8}$ of the jar with yellow stones, and $\frac{4}{8}$ of the jar with purple stones. How much of the jar is filled in all?

What do I know?   Pippa filled $\frac{1}{8}$, $\frac{2}{8}$, and $\frac{4}{8}$ of a jar.

What am I asked to find?   How much of the jar is filled with stones?

Plan   Draw a picture and write an equation.

$$\frac{1}{8} + \frac{2}{8} + \frac{4}{8} = x$$

Solve   Find equal fractions and add. Simplify if you need to.

$$\frac{1}{8} + \frac{2}{8} + \frac{4}{8} = \frac{7}{8}$$
$$x = \frac{7}{8}$$

Pippa filled the jar $\frac{7}{8}$ full of stones.

Draw a picture and write an equation to solve.

1. Joel walked $\frac{4}{12}$ of a mile to the store, $\frac{3}{12}$ of a mile to the library, and $\frac{2}{12}$ of a mile to the post office. Let x = the total distance Joel walked. How far did he walk?

   _____

2. Midge walked $\frac{3}{4}$ mile Monday and $\frac{1}{4}$ mile Tuesday. Let x = how much farther she walked on Monday. How much farther did Midge walk on Monday?

   _____

3. **Number Sense** Glenda wrote $\frac{2}{10}$ of her paper on Monday, $\frac{1}{10}$ of her paper on Tuesday, and $\frac{1}{10}$ of her paper on Wednesday. She said she wrote more than half of her paper. Is she correct? Why or why not?

   _____

   _____

Problem Solving: Draw a Picture and Write an Equation

Draw a picture and write an equation to solve.

1. Jamie bought $\frac{5}{8}$ pound of wheat flour. He also bought $\frac{2}{8}$ pound of white flour. How much flour did he buy?

2. Katie is $\frac{6}{10}$ of the way to Brianna's house. Larry is $\frac{7}{10}$ of the way to Brianna's house. How much closer to Brianna's house is Larry?

3. Nina practiced the trumpet for $\frac{1}{6}$ hour. Santiago practiced the trumpet for $\frac{4}{6}$ hour. How much longer did Santiago practice than Nina?

4. Ned caught $\frac{4}{12}$ pound of fish. Sarah caught $\frac{5}{12}$ pound of fish. Jessa caught $\frac{6}{12}$ pound of fish. Which bar diagram shows how to find how many pounds of fish they caught in all?

5. John had $\frac{5}{8}$ of a pizza left after a party. He gave $\frac{3}{8}$ of the pizza to his friend to take home and he kept the rest. Draw a picture showing what fraction of the pizza John kept, and write an equation to solve.

_____

_____

Name _____

Fractions as Multiples of Unit Fractions: Using Models

Ricardo has an apple that is cut into quarters.

He wants to eat $\frac{3}{4}$ of the apple.

How many $\frac{1}{4}$ pieces does he need to make $\frac{3}{4}$?

Use fraction strips and a number line.

Each fraction strip equals $\frac{1}{4}$.

There are three $\frac{1}{4}$ fraction strips.

$$\frac{3}{4} = 3 \times \frac{1}{4}$$

Ricardo needs three $\frac{1}{4}$ pieces to make $\frac{3}{4}$.

In **1** and **2**, use the number line and fraction strips to complete the equation.

1.

$$\frac{4}{6} = \underline{\hspace{1cm}} \times \underline{\hspace{1cm}}$$

2.

$$\frac{7}{8} = \underline{\hspace{1cm}} \times \underline{\hspace{1cm}}$$

Fractions as Multiples of Unit Fractions: Using Models

For **1** through **9**, write the fraction as a multiple of a unit fraction.
Use fraction strips to help.

1. $\frac{2}{4} =$ _____

2. $\frac{4}{6} =$ _____

3. $\frac{3}{5} =$ _____

4. $\frac{3}{3} =$ _____

5. $\frac{7}{8} =$ _____

6. $\frac{6}{2} =$ _____

7. $\frac{5}{6} =$ _____

8. $\frac{9}{5} =$ _____

9. $\frac{8}{3} =$ _____

10. Use the picture at the right to write a
multiplication equation with $\frac{1}{2}$ as a factor.
Explain how you found the answer.

_____

_____

_____

11. How can you tell that a fraction is a unit fraction?

_____

_____

12. Which equation describes the picture?

A $\frac{1}{5} = 5 \times \frac{1}{2}$

C $\frac{5}{2} = 5 \times \frac{1}{5}$

B $\frac{1}{2} = 5 \times \frac{1}{2}$

D $\frac{5}{2} = 5 \times \frac{1}{2}$

Multiplying a Fraction by a Whole Number: Using Models

Write a multiplication equation of a whole number times a fraction to go with the picture.

$\frac{1}{5}$	$\frac{1}{5}$	$\frac{1}{5}$	$\frac{1}{5}$	$\frac{1}{5}$	$\frac{1}{5}$

Find the unit fraction: $\frac{1}{5}$

Count the number of unit fractions: 6

Write a multiplication equation to show the number of unit fractions times the unit fraction. $6 \times \frac{1}{5} = \blacksquare$

Multiply to find the product. $6 \times \frac{1}{5} = \frac{6}{5}$

The multiplication equation that goes with the picture is $6 \times \frac{1}{5} = \frac{6}{5}$.

In **1–2**, write a multiplication equation of a whole number and a fraction to go with the picture.

1.

$\frac{1}{3}$	$\frac{1}{3}$	$\frac{1}{3}$	$\frac{1}{3}$	$\frac{1}{3}$	$\frac{1}{3}$	$\frac{1}{3}$	$\frac{1}{3}$

Unit fraction: _____

Number of unit fractions: _____

Multiplication equation: _____

2.

$\frac{1}{4}$	$\frac{1}{4}$	$\frac{1}{4}$	$\frac{1}{4}$	$\frac{1}{4}$	$\frac{1}{4}$	$\frac{1}{4}$	$\frac{1}{4}$	$\frac{1}{4}$

Unit fraction: _____

Number of unit fractions: _____

Multiplication equation: _____

Multiplying a Fraction by a Whole Number: Using Models

For **1–3**, use each model to write a multiplication equation with a whole number and a fraction.

1.

$\frac{5}{6}$ $\frac{5}{6}$

_____

2.

_____

3.

$\frac{3}{10}$ $\frac{3}{10}$ $\frac{3}{10}$

_____

4. Reason Write a multiplication equation of a whole number times a fraction to go with the number line.

_____

5. Model Explain why $4 \times \frac{3}{5} = \frac{(4 \times 3)}{5} = \frac{12}{5}$. Draw a picture.

_____

_____

6. Audrey uses $\frac{5}{8}$ cup of fruit in each smoothie she makes. She makes 6 smoothies to share with her friends. How many cups of fruit does she use?

$\frac{5}{8}$	$\frac{5}{8}$	$\frac{5}{8}$	$\frac{5}{8}$	$\frac{5}{8}$	$\frac{5}{8}$

A $3\frac{3}{8}$ cups   **C** $3\frac{3}{4}$ cups

B $3\frac{1}{2}$ cups   **D** $6\frac{5}{8}$ cups

Name _____

Multiplying a Fraction by a Whole Number: Using Symbols

Josh has 4 pieces of rope. Each piece of rope is $\frac{3}{4}$ yard long. How many yards of rope does Josh have?

You can think of each piece of rope as a separate group. The size of each group is $\frac{3}{4}$ yard.

$$\frac{3}{4} + \frac{3}{4} + \frac{3}{4} + \frac{3}{4}$$

Since all of the groups are the same size, you can use multiplication to find the total.

$$4 \times \frac{3}{4} = \frac{(4 \times 3)}{4} = \frac{12}{4} = 3$$

Josh has 3 yards of rope.

Think: The number of groups times the size of each group.

Solve. Show your work.

1. Mia is painting her room. Her room has 4 walls. Each wall uses $\frac{2}{3}$ gallon of paint. How much paint does she need to paint all of her walls?

   $$\frac{2}{3} + \frac{2}{3} + \frac{2}{3} + \frac{2}{3} = 4 \times \frac{2}{3}$$

   $4 \times \frac{2}{3} = $ _____

2. Nat has 5 pieces of string. Each piece is $\frac{7}{8}$ inch long. How many inches of string does Nat have?

   $$\frac{7}{8} + \frac{7}{8} + \frac{7}{8} + \frac{7}{8} + \frac{7}{8} = 5 \times \frac{7}{8}$$

   $5 \times \frac{7}{8} = $ _____

3. Caroline is making 8 batches of biscuits. Each batch uses $\frac{5}{6}$ cup of flour. How many cups of flour does Caroline need?

   _____

   _____

Multiplying a Fraction by a Whole Number: Using Symbols

For **1–8**, multiply.

1. $8 \times \frac{5}{12} =$ _____

2. $9 \times \frac{1}{4} =$ _____

3. $5 \times \frac{3}{5} =$ _____

4. $10 \times \frac{5}{6} =$ _____

5. $9 \times \frac{3}{10} =$ _____

6. $7 \times \frac{1}{3} =$ _____

7. $12 \times \frac{1}{5} =$ _____

8. $11 \times \frac{7}{8} =$ _____

9. Model Matt is raking leaves for his neighbors. It takes him $\frac{7}{8}$ hour to rake the leaves in one lawn. How long will it take Matt to rake the leaves for 6 neighbors? Write a multiplication sentence to solve.

_____

10. Zoey is making bracelets for her friends. Each bracelet takes $\frac{5}{6}$ foot of string. How much string will Zoey need to make 12 bracelets?

_____

11. Farid takes $\frac{7}{8}$ teaspoon of allergy medicine every day. How much medicine will he take in one week?

A $1\frac{3}{4}$ teaspoons   **B** $5\frac{1}{4}$ teaspoons   **C** $6\frac{1}{8}$ teaspoons   **D** $7\frac{7}{8}$ teaspoons

12. Writing to Explain Mrs. Nunez is correcting math tests. She corrects 7 tests before school, and 5 tests after school. If each test takes her $\frac{1}{5}$ hour to correct, how long will it take Mrs. Nunez to correct the tests? Explain.

_____

_____

_____

Any fraction that has a denominator of 10 or 100 can be written as a decimal. Tenths and hundredths are written as digits to the right of the decimal point.

The shaded part is $\frac{2}{10}$ of the whole area.

Write it as a decimal: 0.2

Say: two tenths.

The shaded part is $\frac{13}{100}$ of the whole area.

Write it as a decimal: 0.13

Say: thirteen hundredths

Write a fraction and a decimal to tell how much is shaded.

1.

2.

3. How are the two shaded grids alike? How are they different?

_____

_____

_____

_____

Write each fraction as a decimal.

4. $\frac{3}{10}$ **5.** $\frac{9}{10}$ **6.** $\frac{9}{100}$ **7.** $\frac{27}{100}$

_____   _____   _____   _____

Write each decimal as a fraction in its simplest form.

8. 0.40   **9.** 0.76   **10.** 4.8   **11.** 0.07

_____   _____   _____   _____

Fractions and Decimals

Write a fraction and a decimal to show how much is shaded.

1.

_____

2.

_____

3.

_____

Draw a model that shows each decimal.

4. 0.16

5. 1.7

6. 0.78

Write each fraction as a decimal.

7. $\frac{1}{100}$

8. $9\frac{4}{10}$

9. $\frac{6}{10}$

10. $\frac{17}{100}$

_____   _____   _____   _____

Write each decimal as a fraction in its simplest form.

11. 0.5

12. 0.70

13. 0.3

14. 3.60

_____   _____   _____   _____

15. In the decimal models, how many strips equal 10 small squares?

   A 70 strips   **B** 10 strips   **C** 7 strips   **D** 1 strip

16. Writing to Explain Explain the steps you would take to write $\frac{36}{10}$ as a decimal.

_____

_____

_____

Fractions and Decimals on the Number Line

How do you locate fractions and decimals on a number line?

Show $\frac{1}{8}$ on a number line.

Draw a number line and label 0 and 1. Divide the distance from 0 to 1 into 8 equal lengths.

Label 0, $\frac{1}{8}$, $\frac{2}{8}$, $\frac{3}{8}$, $\frac{4}{8}$, $\frac{5}{8}$, $\frac{6}{8}$, $\frac{7}{8}$, and 1.

Draw a point at $\frac{1}{8}$.

Show 0.3 on another number line.

Draw another number line and label 0 and 1. Divide the distance from 0 to 1 into 10 equal lengths.

Label 0.1, 0.2, 0.3, 0.4, and so on.

Use the number line to name the fraction that should be written at each point.

1. A _____ **2.** B _____ **3.** C _____ **4.** D _____

Identify the correct point on the number line for each fraction or decimal.

5. $6\frac{1}{3}$ _____ **6.** 5.3 _____ **7.** $5\frac{2}{3}$ _____ **8.** 6.8 _____

Fractions and Decimals on the Number Line

Use the number line to name the fraction or decimal that should be written at each point.

1. E _____   **2.** F _____   **3.** G _____   **4.** H _____

Identify the correct point on the number line for each fraction or decimal.

5. 8.3 _____   **6.** $7\frac{3}{5}$ _____   **7.** 7.7 _____   **8.** 8.2 _____

9. Eamon used a number line to compare two numbers, 0.48 and $\frac{3}{5}$. One number was less than $\frac{1}{2}$ and the other number was greater than $\frac{1}{2}$. Which number was less than $\frac{1}{2}$? _____

10. Writing to Explain Jayne says that 0.45 is equal to $\frac{4}{10}$. Is she correct? Explain.

_____

_____

_____

Name _____

Equivalent Fractions and Decimals

A fraction and a decimal can both be used to represent the same value.

Write $\frac{6}{12}$ as a decimal.

Step 1 Write the fraction in simplest form.

$$\frac{6}{12} = \frac{1}{2}$$

Step 2 Rename the fraction using a denominator of 10, 100, or 1,000.

Think: What number times 2 equals 10?

Step 3 Write the decimal.

$\frac{5}{10}$ is five tenths.

$$\frac{5}{10} = 0.5$$

So, $\frac{6}{12} = 0.5$

In **1** through **4**, find the missing numbers. Then write each fraction as a decimal.

1. $\frac{1}{4} = \frac{\square}{100}$

2. $\frac{9}{20} = \frac{\square}{100}$

3. $\frac{3}{15} = \frac{1}{\square} = \frac{\square}{10}$

4. $\frac{8}{25} = \frac{\square}{100}$

_____ _____ _____ _____

Write each fraction as a decimal.

5. $\frac{4}{5}$

6. $\frac{4}{50}$

7. $\frac{4}{25}$

8. $\frac{13}{20}$

9. $\frac{9}{50}$

_____ _____ _____ _____ _____

Tell whether each pair shows equivalent numbers.

10. $\frac{2}{5}$; 0.25

11. $\frac{10}{25}$; 0.4

12. $\frac{3}{5}$; 0.35

13. $\frac{7}{20}$; 0.35

_____ _____ _____ _____

14. Nine out of 15, or $\frac{9}{15}$, of the people at the skating rink brought their own skates. Write an equivalent decimal for $\frac{9}{15}$. _____

Name _____

Equivalent Fractions and Decimals

In **1** through **5**, write each fraction as a decimal.

1. $\frac{1}{5}$ **2.** $\frac{9}{12}$ **3.** $\frac{11}{25}$ **4.** $\frac{19}{20}$ **5.** $\frac{23}{50}$

_____ _____ _____ _____ _____

In **6** through **9**, tell whether each pair shows equivalent numbers.

6. $\frac{2}{5}$; 0.5 **7.** $\frac{7}{20}$; 0.07 **8.** $\frac{4}{16}$; 0.25 **9.** $\frac{11}{50}$; 0.22

_____ _____ _____ _____

10. A rock band has 5 members, and $\frac{2}{5}$ of the members play string instruments. Also, 0.4 of the members sing. Does the band have the same number of string instrument players as singers? Explain.

11. Kevin has 20 words to learn for his spelling test on Friday. He has learned 6 of the words. So, he has learned $\frac{6}{20}$ of the words. Write $\frac{6}{20}$ in simplest form, and find an equivalent decimal.

_____

12. Which decimal is equivalent to $\frac{5}{20}$?

   A 0.20   **C** 0.35

   B 0.25   **D** 0.52

13. Gina wrote that $\frac{4}{5}$ is greater than 0.75. Is Gina correct? Explain why or why not.

_____

14. Look at Exercise 8. Explain how you decided whether the numbers are equivalent.

_____

_____

_____

Decimal Place Value

A grid can be used to show tenths and hundredths. To show 0.3, you would shade 3 out of the 10 parts.

0.3
3 out of 10 parts are shaded.

To show 0.30, you would shade 30 out of the 100 parts.

0.30
30 out of 100 parts are shaded.

One part of the hundredths grid can be compared to a penny, since one part of the grid is equal to 0.01 and a penny is equal to one hundredth of a dollar.

Tenths and hundredths are related. In the above examples, 3 tenths or 30 hundredths of the grids are shaded, or 0.3 and 0.30. These numbers are equal: 0.3 = 0.30.

Write the word form and decimal for each shaded part.

1.

_____

2.

_____

Shade each grid to show the decimal.

3. 0.57

4. 0.4

5. Number Sense Which is greater, 0.04 or 0.4? Explain.

_____

_____

_____

_____

Decimal Place Value

Write the word form and decimal for each shaded part.

1.

_____

2.

_____

For each fact, shade a grid to show the part of the population of
each country that lives in cities.

3. In Jamaica, 0.5
of the people live
in cities.

4. Only 0.11 of the
population of
Uganda live in cities.

5. In Norway, 0.72 of
the people live
in cities.

6. Which grid shows fourteen hundredths?

A   **B**   **C**   **D**

7. Writing to Explain Explain why one column in a hundredths
grid is equal to one column in a tenths grid.

_____

_____

_____

Comparing and Ordering Decimals

Compare 0.87 to 0.89.

First, begin at the left. Find the first place where the numbers are different.

0.87

0.89

The numbers are the same in the tenths place, so look to the next place.

The first place where the numbers are different is the hundredths place. Compare 7 hundredths to 9 hundredths.

0.07 < 0.09, so 0.87 < 0.89

Compare. Write >, <, or = for each $\bigcirc$.

1. 0.36 $\bigcirc$ 0.76 **2.** 5.1 $\bigcirc$ 5.01 **3.** 1.2 $\bigcirc$ 1.20

4. 6.55 $\bigcirc$ 6.6 **5.** 0.62 $\bigcirc$ 0.82 **6.** 4.71 $\bigcirc$ 4.17

Order the numbers from least to greatest.

7. 1.36, 1.3, 1.63 **8.** 0.42, 3.74, 3.47

_____ _____

9. 6.46, 6.41, 4.6 **10.** 0.3, 0.13, 0.19, 0.31

_____ _____

11. Number Sense Which is greater, 8.0 or 0.8? Explain.

_____

_____

_____

Comparing and Ordering Decimals

Compare. Write >, <, or = for each ◯.

1. 0.31 ◯ 0.41

2. 1.9 ◯ 0.95

3. 0.09 ◯ 0.1

4. 2.70 ◯ 2.7

5. 0.81 ◯ 0.79

6. 2.12 ◯ 2.21

Order the numbers from least to greatest.

7. 0.37, 0.41, 0.31

8. 1.16, 1.61, 6.11

_____

_____

9. 7.9, 7.91, 7.09, 7.19

10. 1.45, 1.76, 1.47, 1.67

_____

_____

Margaret has three cats. Sophie weighs 4.27 lb, Tigger weighs 6.25 lb, and Ghost weighs 4.7 lb.

11. Which cat has the greatest weight? _____

12. Which cat weighs the least? _____

13. Which group of numbers is ordered from least to greatest?

   A 0.12, 1.51, 0.65

   B 5.71, 5.4, 0.54

   C 0.4, 0.09, 0.41

   D 0.05, 0.51, 1.5

14. **Writing to Explain** Darrin put the numbers 7.25, 7.52, 5.72, and 5.27 in order from greatest to least. Is his work correct? Explain.

_____

_____

Using Money
to Understand Decimals

We can use money to understand decimals. For example, a dime
is one-tenth of a dollar, or 0.1. It takes 10 dimes to equal a dollar.
A penny is one one-hundredth of a dollar, or 0.01, so it takes
100 pennies to equal one dollar.

| $0.01 | $0.05 | $0.10 | $0.25 | $0.50 |
| 0.01 | 0.05 | 0.1 | 0.25 | 0.5 |

The decimal point is read by saying "and." So, $1.99 is read as
"one dollar *and* ninety-nine cents."

1. $3.52 = _____ dollars + _____ dimes + _____ pennies

2. $1.87 = _____ dollar + _____ dimes + _____ pennies

3. **Number Sense** Write nine and thirty-six hundredths
   with a decimal point.   _____

How could you use only dollars,
dimes, and pennies to buy

4. the baseball?

   _____

   _____

5. the baseball bat?

   _____

   _____

$3.99

$8.49

$12.20

Using Money to Understand Decimals

1. 2.18 = _____ ones + _____ tenth + _____ hundredths

   $2.18 = _____ dollars + _____ dime + _____ pennies

2. 9.27 = _____ ones + _____ hundredths

   $9.27 = _____ dollars + _____ pennies

3. 7.39 = _____ ones + _____ tenths + _____ hundredths

   $7.39 = _____ dollars + _____ dimes + _____ pennies

4. **Number Sense** Write 3 dollars, 9 dimes, and 5 pennies with a dollar sign and decimal point.

   _____

5. **Number Sense** If you have 5 tenths of a dollar, how much money do you have?

   _____

6. Lana wants to buy a book for $6.95. How can she pay for the book using only dollars, dimes, and nickels?

   _____

7. How would you write sixteen and twenty-five hundredths with a decimal point?

   A 16.025   **B** 16.25   **C** 162.5   **D** 1,625

8. **Writing to Explain** Which is greater, 4 tenths and 2 hundredths or 2 tenths and 4 hundredths? Explain.

   _____

   _____

Problem Solving:
Draw a Picture

A fence is 20 ft long. It has posts at each end and at every 4 ft along its length. How many fence posts are there?

Read and Understand

Step 1: What do you know?

The fence is 20 ft long.

There are fence posts at each end.

There are fence posts every 4 ft along the length of the fence.

Step 2: What are you trying to find?

How many posts the fence has.

Plan and Solve

Step 3: What strategy will you use?

Strategy: Draw a picture

There are 6 fence posts altogether.

Look Back and Check

Step 4: Is your work correct?

Yes, the picture shows that there is a total of 6 fence posts.

Solve the problem. Write the answer in a complete sentence.

1. Tim, Kara, and Ann are working together to write a 4-page report. Each student is going to do an equal amount of writing. What fraction of the entire report does each student need to write?

Problem Solving:
Draw a Picture

Solve each problem. Write the answer in a complete sentence.

1. Three friends divided a veggie pizza into 12 slices. If they divide the pizza equally, what fraction of the pizza would each friend get?

_____

2. Mark is making a quilt with his grandmother. Each row of the quilt has 6 squares. There are 8 rows. $\frac{1}{2}$ of the squares are blue. How many blue squares are in the quilt?

_____

3. Jane pulled weeds in the garden 7 times. She was paid $5 each time she pulled weeds for less than 1 hour and $6 each time she pulled weeds for more than 1 hour. If Jane received $39, how many times did she pull weeds for more than 1 hour?

_____

_____

4. Neil needs to cut 3 long boards into 9 smaller boards. The first is 10 ft, the second is 16 ft, and the third is 18 ft. The table lists the smaller boards Neil needs. Use a drawing to show how he can divide the 3 boards so there is no waste.

Length of Board	Number Needed
4 ft	3
5 ft	4
6 ft	2

10 ft

16 ft

18 ft

Name _____

Customary Units of Length

Unit	**Example**
inch	width of a U.S. quarter
1 foot (ft) = 12 inches (in.)	gym shoes
1 yard (yd) = 3 feet	height of a desk
1 mile (mi) = 5,280 feet	distance between school and home

How to measure an object:

To measure an object, make sure one end of the object begins at the zero unit.

The rectangle is closest to the 2 in. mark, so we can say the rectangle is 2 in. long to the nearest inch.

Choose the most appropriate unit to measure the length of each.
Write in., ft, yd, or mi.

1. cat _____

2. lake _____

3. hallway _____

4. basketball court _____

Estimate first. Then, find each length to the nearest inch.

5. ⊢————————————————⊣ _____

6. ⊢————⊣ _____

Name _____

Customary Units of Length

Choose the most appropriate unit to measure the length of each. Write in., ft, yd, or mi.

1. boat _____

2. wallet _____

3. soccer field _____

4. finger bandage _____

5. computer cable _____

6. train route _____

7. nose _____

8. sea _____

Estimate first. Then, measure each length to the nearest inch.

9. ├──────────────┤ _____

10. ├──────┤ _____

11. Use a ruler to find the length of one side of the triangle. Then find the perimeter.

_____

12. Eileen needs 9 feet of fabric to make a skirt. If Eileen has 18 feet of fabric how many skirts can she make?

_____

13. Which unit would be most appropriate for measuring the length of a barn?

A inches   **B** pounds   **C** yards   **D** miles

14. Writing to Explain Explain how you would decide which unit is best for measuring your math book.

_____

_____

Customary Units of Capacity

Capacity is the amount that a container can hold. Capacity is measured in teaspoons, tablespoons, fluid ounces, cups, pints, quarts, and gallons, from smallest to largest.

| a cup | There are 2 cups in a pint. | There are 2 pints in a quart. | There are 4 quarts in a gallon. |

Choose the most appropriate unit or units to measure the capacity of each. Write fl oz, c, pt, qt, or gal.

1. water bottle _____

2. bathtub _____

3. milk carton _____

4. coffee pot _____

5. teacup _____

6. jug of juice _____

7. Reasoning Would a cup be a good tool for measuring the amount of water in a bathtub? Explain why or why not.

_____

_____

The adult human body contains about 5 qt of blood.

8. Are there more or less than 5 pt of blood in a human adult?

_____

9. Are there more or less than 5 gal of blood in a human adult?

_____

Customary Units of Capacity

Choose the most appropriate unit or units to measure the
capacity of each. Write tsp, tbsp, fl oz, c, pt, qt, or gal.

1. teacup _____

2. juice box _____

3. motor oil _____

4. salt in a recipe _____

5. carton of cream _____

6. large watering can _____

7. **Number Sense** Would a teaspoon be a good way to
measure the capacity of a milk carton? Explain.

_____

_____

8. A jug for the baseball team holds 20 gal of
water. To make an energy drink, 1 c of mix is
used for every 2 gal of water. How many cups
of the mix are needed to fill the jug with energy
drink? _____

9. Which unit has the greatest capacity?

   A Tablespoon   **C** Pint

   B Quart   **D** Teaspoon

10. **Writing to Explain** Cassidy says that capacity is the same
as the amount. Do you agree? Explain why or why not.

_____

_____

_____

Name _____

Units of Weight

There are 16 ounces (oz) in 1 pound (lb).

There are 2,000 lb in 1 ton (T).

You use ounces to weigh smaller things, like a tomato.

You use pounds to weigh things like a heavy box.

You use tons to weigh very large or heavy things, like a rocket.

tomato

Choose the most appropriate unit to measure the weight of each.
Write oz, lb, or T.

1. car _____
2. computer _____

3. bowling ball _____
4. onion _____

5. Tyrannosaurus rex _____
6. vacuum cleaner _____

7. **Reasoning** A hippo weighs about 5,000 lb. Does the same hippo weigh more or less than 5,000 oz?

_____

8. Would you most likely measure a leaf using ounces, pounds, or tons? Explain.

_____

_____

_____

Units of Weight

Choose the most appropriate unit to measure the weight of each.
Write oz, lb, or T.

1. truck _____

2. can of vegetables _____

3. person _____

4. desk _____

5. trailer full of bricks _____

6. cup of flour _____

7. box of paper _____

8. CD _____

9. **Reasoning** Would a scale that is used to weigh food be the
   best tool to weigh concrete blocks? Explain why or why not.

   _____

   _____

   _____

10. Jen wants to weigh her cat. What is the most
    appropriate unit she should use to weigh the
    cat, ounces, pounds, or tons? _____

11. What is the most appropriate unit you would
    use to measure the weight of a house? _____

12. Which animal would it be appropriate to measure its weight in ounces?

    A mouse   **B** elephant   **C** horse   **D** cow

13. **Writing to Explain** Dezi says that there are more ounces in
    1 T than there are pounds. Do you agree? Explain.

    _____

    _____

    _____

Name _____

Changing Customary Units

Here is a table of the customary units of length, capacity, and weight. Use the table to change one customary unit of measure to another.

Customary Units		
Length	**Capacity**	**Weight**
1 ft = 12 in.	1 tbsp = 3 tsp	1 lb = 16 oz
1 yd = 36 in.	1 fl oz = 2 tbsp	1 T = 2,000 lb
1 yd = 3 ft	1 c = 8 fl oz	
1 mi = 5,280 ft	1 pt = 2 c	
1 mi = 1,760 yd	1 qt = 2 pt	
	1 gal = 4 qt	

Remember: When converting from lesser to greater units, you divide. When converting from greater to lesser units, you multiply.

Which distance is longer, 100 in. or 10 yd?

1 yd = 3 ft   3 ft (12 in./ft) = 36 in.
10 yd at (36 in./yd) = 360 in.

360 in. is larger than 100 in., so 10 yd is longer.

1. Which is longer, 6 ft or 70 in.?   _____

2. How many pints is 24 quarts?   _____

3. Which weighs more, 5 lb or 100 oz?   _____

4. If a recipe calls for 2 tbsp, how many tsp is that?   _____

Name _____

Changing Customary Units

For **1** through **12**, compare. Write >, <, or = for each ◯.

1. 1 yd ◯ 4 ft   **2.** 40 in. ◯ 1 yd

3. 6 pt ◯ 3 qt   **4.** 3 lb ◯ 50 oz

5. 2 yd ◯ 6 ft   **6.** 3 ft ◯ 30 in.

7. 1 gal ◯ 15 c   **8.** 3 T ◯ 3,000 lb

9. 1 mi ◯ 2,000 yd   **10.** 100 ft ◯ 100 mi

11. 1 gal ◯ 100 fl oz   **12.** 3 tbsp ◯ 10 tsp

13. Which measurement is **NOT** equal to 1 mile?

   A 1,760 yd   **B** 5,280 yd   **C** 5,280 ft   **D** 63,360 in.

14. Writing to Explain A recipe calls for 4 tsp of baking soda
   and 1 fl oz of vanilla. Which measurement is greater? Explain.

   _____

   _____

   _____

Problem Solving: Writing to Explain

Explaining your problem-solving strategy can help you solve problems and avoid errors.

Jessy and Dean each measured the weight of their pets. Jessy's dog weighs 12 pounds 2 ounces. Dean's cat weighs 128 ounces. Dean said his cat weighed more. Is he correct?

PLAN	First, I need to convert Jessy's measurement to ounces so I can compare the weights of her dog and Dean's cat.	Jessy's measurement: 12 pounds 2 ounces I remember that 1 pound = 16 ounces. 12 pounds x 16 ounces = 192 ounces. So, 12 pounds 2 ounces = 192 ounces + 2 ounces 192 + 2 = 194 ounces
SOLVE	Compare measurements. Dean's cat weighs 128 ounces. Jessy's dog weighs 194 ounces.	Dean was incorrect. His cat weighs 128 ounces and Jessy's dog weighs 194 ounces. Jessy's dog weighs more. Dean may not have remembered that each pound equals 16 ounces.

Solve the problems below and explain how you found your answers.

1. Raul measures the length of a hallway upstairs as 8 feet. His brother measures the length of a hallway downstairs as 96 inches. Which hallway is longer?

   _____

   _____

   _____

   _____

2. **Number Sense** Sue knows that the perimeter of the triangle to the right is 13 inches. Can she find the length of the missing side? Explain.

   5 in.   ? in.
   3 in.

   _____

   _____

   _____

Problem Solving:
Writing to Explain

1. The shape to the right is a rectangle. How can you use the information shown to find its perimeter?

Area = 35 in.^{2}

← 7 in. →

_____

_____

2. David took a survey of 12 people to find out what their favorite animal is. Of those, $\frac{1}{3}$ of the people said they like dogs best. How can you find out how many people liked dogs best?

_____

_____

3. Between 6 A.M. and 10 A.M. the temperature rose by 5°F. Between 10 A.M. and 2 P.M. the temperature rose by 6°F. Between 2 P.M. and 6 P.M. the temperature rose by 0°C. Would you be able to tell how much the temperature rose since 6 A.M.? Why or why not?

_____

_____

4. How could you find out which weighs more, one ton of pillows or one ton of bowling balls?

_____

_____

5. Warren measured a rectangular window to find out how much plastic he would need to cover it. The window measured 5 ft 6 inches by 2 ft 9 inches. About how many square inches of plastic does Warren need to cover the window?

A 1,800 square inches   C 2,400 square inches

B 2,100 square inches   D 2,800 square inches

Name _____

Using Metric Units of Length

Metric units are used to estimate and measure length.

Metric Units of Length

    1 cm = 10 mm

    1 dm = 10 cm

    1 m = 100 cm

    1 km = 1,000 m

Find the length to the nearest centimeter.

Measured to the nearest centimeter, the segment is 6 cm long.

Choose the most appropriate unit to measure each. Write mm, cm, dm, m, or km.

1. length of a finger _____

2. length of a football _____

3. width of a big toe _____

4. length of the lunchroom _____

5. distance between Paris and London _____

Estimate first. Then, find each length to the nearest centimeter.

6. ├───────────────────────────┤
_____, _____

7. ├────────────┤
_____, _____

8. **Number Sense** The distance across a field is 20 m. Is the distance across the same field greater than or less than 20 km?

_____

Using Metric Units of Length

Choose the most appropriate unit to measure each. Write mm, cm, dm, m, or km.

1. width of a house

_____

2. distance across Lake Erie

_____

3. width of a thumbtack

_____

4. thickness of a phone book

_____

Estimate first. Then, find each length to the nearest centimeter.

5. ├─────────────────┤

_____, _____

6. ├──────┤

_____, _____

7. Number Sense Which would you be more likely to measure in centimeters, a fish tank or a swimming pool?

_____

8. Which is longer, a 12 cm pencil or a 1 dm pen? _____

9. Which is the most appropriate measure for the length of a skateboard?

A 5 mm   **B** 5 cm   **C** 5 dm   **D** 5 m

10. Writing to Explain Jill measured the length of her eraser. She wrote 5 on her paper without the unit. Which metric unit of measure should Jill include?

_____

_____

_____

Metric Units of Capacity

Capacity is the amount of liquid that an object can hold. The metric system of measurement uses the units liter (L) and milliliter (mL).

You would use liters to measure the amount of water in a water bottle or the amount of gasoline in a gas can.

A milliliter is a very small unit of measurement. There are 5 mL of liquid in a teaspoon. You would use milliliters to measure small amounts of liquid, such as measuring how much medicine to give a baby.

1 L is the same as 1,000 mL.

Choose the most appropriate unit to use to measure the capacity of each. Write L or mL.

1. thimble _____

2. kitchen sink _____

3. coffee cup _____

4. bucket of water for a horse _____

5. **Number Sense** A container holds 5 L of fluid. Does it hold more than or less than 5 mL of fluid?

_____

6. A bottle is filled with saline solution for eyes. Is the bottle more likely to hold 15 mL of solution or 1 L of solution?

_____

Metric Units of Capacity

Choose the most appropriate unit to measure the capacity
of each. Write L or mL.

1. water in a bathtub   2. perfume in a bottle   3. soup in a can

_____   _____   _____

4. **Number Sense** Which will be less, the number of
   liters or the number of milliliters, of water in a pool?   _____

5. Name something you might measure in liters.

   _____

6. Name something you might measure in milliliters.

   _____

7. A gallon of milk is about the same as 4 L of milk.
   About how many liters of milk are there in 10 gal?   _____

8. A small can of tomato juice contains 56 mL
   of juice. A large can of tomato juice contains
   202 mL of juice. How much juice is there in the
   large and small can combined?   _____

9. Which capacity would you be most likely to measure in milliliters?

   A gas in a car   C tea in a cup

   B water in a bathtub   D detergent in a bottle

10. **Writing to Explain** Would you be more likely to measure the
    amount of water in your kitchen sink in liters or milliliters? Explain.

    _____

    _____

Units of Mass

The metric units for mass are grams (g) and kilograms (kg).

1 kg = 1,000 g

A cherry or a pen might have a mass of 1 g.

A kitten or watermelon might have a mass of 1 kg.

Choose the most appropriate unit to measure the mass of each.
Write g or kg.

1. lawn mower _____

2. pumpkin _____

3. child _____

4. gold ring _____

5. robin's egg _____

6. cannonball _____

7. cement block _____

8. spool of thread _____

9. Number Sense Which is greater, 850 g or 1 kg?

_____

10. The mass of a certain window is 18 kg. What is the mass of
5 of those windows?

_____

_____

11. The mass of a horse is 180 kg. The mass of a second
horse is 275 kg. How much larger is the mass of the
second horse than that of the first horse?

_____

_____

_____

Units of Mass

Choose the most appropriate unit to measure the mass of each.
Write g or kg.

1. banana _____

2. tractor _____

3. coin _____

4. bowling ball _____

5. letter _____

6. encyclopedia _____

7. Number Sense Which is a greater number, the mass of a
cat in grams or the mass of the same cat in kilograms?

_____

8. The *Dromornis stirtoni* was once the largest
living bird. It is now extinct. The ostrich is
now the largest living bird. What is the
difference in mass between the *Dromornis
stirtoni* and the ostrich?

Bird	Mass
Ostrich	156 kg
Andean condor	9 kg
Eurasian eagle owl	4.2 kg
Dromornis stirtoni	454 kg

_____

9. Which has a larger mass, an Andean condor or a Eurasian
eagle owl?

_____

10. Which object would be most likely to have a mass of 2 kg?

A A truck   **B** An orange   **C** A mosquito   **D** A math book

11. Writing to Explain Would you be more likely to find the
mass of a pen in grams or in kilograms? Explain.

_____

_____

_____

Changing Metric Units

Here is a table of the conversion factors for metric units.

Metric Measures

1 cm = 10 mm
1 dm = 10 cm
1 m = 100 cm
1 m = 1,000 mm
1 km = 1,000 m
1 L = 1,000 mL
1 kg = 1,000 g

Remember: When converting from lesser to greater units you divide. When converting from greater to lesser units you multiply.

Which has more mass, a kilogram of lead or 1,200 grams of bricks?

1 kg = 1,000 g
1,000 g of lead is less than 1,200 g of bricks.
The bricks have more mass.

Solve.

1. Which is greater, 200 mm or 1 m? _____

2. Which amount is less 250 mL
   or 250 L? _____

3. If 4 apples have a mass of 1 kg,
   about how many grams is each
   apple? _____

Name _____

Changing Metric Units

For **1** through **12**, compare. Write >, <, or = for each ◯.

1. 4 m ◯ 400 dm
2. 4 dm ◯ 40 cm

3. 10 L ◯ 1,000 mL
4. 2 kg ◯ 1,500 g

5. 15 cm ◯ 150 mm
6. 1 km ◯ 999 m

7. 4 L ◯ 4,500 mL
8. 500 g ◯ 5 kg

9. 6 km ◯ 6,000 m
10. 200 cm ◯ 3 m

11. 3,000 m ◯ 2 km
12. 100 mm ◯ 1 dm

13. Which measurement is **NOT** equal to 3 m?

   A 30 dm   **B** 300 cm   **C** 3,000 mm   **D** 3,000 cm

14. **Writing to Explain** If 5 potatoes together have a mass
   of 1 kilogram and 8 pears together have a mass of 1,200
   grams, which has the greater mass, a potato or a pear?
   Explain.

   _____

   _____

   _____

Name _____

Units of Time

You can use the information in the table to compare different amounts of time. For example:

Which is longer, 3 years or
40 months?

According to the table,
1 year = 12 months.

Units of Time
1 minute = 60 seconds
1 hour = 60 minutes
1 day = 24 hours
1 week = 7 days
1 month = about 4 weeks
1 year = 52 weeks
1 year = 12 months
1 year = 365 days
1 leap year = 366 days
1 decade = 10 years
1 century = 100 years
1 millennium = 1,000 years

1 year = 12 months
3 years = 36 months

$$\begin{array}{r} 12 \\ \times\ 3 \\ \hline 36 \end{array}$$

40 months > 36 months
40 months > 3 years

So, 40 months is longer
than 3 years.

Write <, >, or = for each $\bigcirc$.

1. 1 year $\bigcirc$ 350 days

2. 25 months $\bigcirc$ 2 years

3. 20 decades $\bigcirc$ 2 centuries

4. 720 days $\bigcirc$ 2 years

5. 8 decades $\bigcirc$ 1 century

6. 72 hours $\bigcirc$ 3 days

7. 240 minutes $\bigcirc$ 3 hours

8. 3 years $\bigcirc$ 120 months

9. Number Sense How many hours are in 2 days? _____

10. A score is 20 years. How many years is 5 score? _____

11. Dave's goldfish lived for 2 years, 8 months.
Chris's goldfish lived for 35 months. Whose
goldfish lived longer? _____

12. Tree A lived for 6 decades and 5 years.
Tree B lived for 58 years. Which tree lived longer? _____

Name _____

Units of Time

Write >, <, or = for each ◯.

1. 48 hours ◯ 4 days

2. 1 year ◯ 12 months

3. 60 minutes ◯ 2 hours

4. 17 days ◯ 2 weeks

5. 5 months ◯ 40 weeks

6. 1 millennium ◯ 10 centuries

7. 6 decades ◯ 1 century

8. 5 decades ◯ 48 years

9. Cheryl's grandparents have been married for 6 decades. How many years have they been married? _____

10. Tom was in elementary school from 1997 to 2002. How much time was that in years? _____

The Declaration of Independence was signed on July 4, 1776. The United States celebrated the bicentennial on July 4, 1976. How much time was that in

11. years? _____

12. decades? _____

13. 49 days = ☐

A 5 weeks   **B** 6 weeks   **C** 7 weeks   **D** 8 weeks

14. Writing to Explain Which is longer: 180 sec or 3 min? Explain how you decided.

_____

_____

_____

Problem Solving: Work Backward

Morning Routine Brenda takes 30 minutes to get dressed for school. She eats breakfast for 20 minutes more, then walks to school. It takes Brenda 15 minutes to walk to school. Brenda needs to be at school by 8:55 A.M. What time is the latest she should get out of bed in the morning?

Read and Understand

Step 1: What do you know?

Brenda takes 30 min to get ready, 20 min for breakfast, and 15 min to walk to school. She must be at school by 8:55 A.M.

Step 2: What are you trying to find?

What time is the latest Brenda should get up?

Plan and Solve

Step 3: What strategy will you use?

Strategy: Work backward.

Work backward from the end, doing the opposite of each step.

I need to work backward, or subtract from the school arrival time, one step at a time.

Brenda must get up by 7:50 A.M. at the latest to make it to school on time.

Look Back and Check

Step 4: Is your work correct?

Yes. If I follow the times forward, I end at 8:55 A.M.

1. When Christopher Columbus was 41 years old he sailed across the Atlantic Ocean for the first time. He went on his final expedition 10 years later, which took 2 years. He died 2 years after his final expedition ended, in 1506. What year was Columbus born?

Problem Solving: Work Backward

Solve by working backward. Write the answer in a complete sentence.

1. There were 21 students in Travis's fourth-grade class at the end of the school year. During the year four new students joined his class, and 2 moved away. One student was transferred to another fourth-grade teacher. How many students were in Travis's class at the beginning of the school year?

   _____

   _____

   _____

2. Sir John Franklin was an explorer who traveled in Canada and the United States. He was 33 years old when he began exploring northwestern Canada. In a second expedition 17 years later, he explored as far as Alaska. 11 years later, Franklin died in an expedition in search of a Northwest Passage in 1847. In what year was Franklin born?

   _____

3. Tessie has a volleyball game at 6:45 P.M. She needs to be there 15 minutes early to warm up for the game, and it takes her 40 minutes to get to the gym. What time should she leave her house?

   _____

4. Frank bought lunch for $5.60 at a diner. He spent $2.00 to ride the bus to the mall and back, and spent $6.50 while he was at the mall. His friend Bill paid him back $5.00 that he had borrowed last week. If Frank arrived at home with $10.50 in his pocket, how much did he have when he left home that morning?

   _____

Solving Perimeter and Area Problems

1. Find the length of the rectangle.

$A =$ _____ and $w =$ _____

$A = \ell \times w$

_____ $= \ell \times$ _____

(Think: If $63 = \ell \times 7$, then $\ell =$ _____ ÷ _____)

$\ell =$ _____

So the length is _____ feet.

7 ft	Area = 63 sq ft

ℓ

2. Find the width of the rectangle.

$P =$ _____ and $\ell =$ _____

$P = 2\ell + 2w$

_____ $= (2 \times$ _____ $) + 2w$

_____ $=$ _____ $+ 2w$ (Think: If $30 = 22 + 2w$, then $2w =$ _____ $-$ _____

$2w =$ _____ (Think: If $2 \times w = 8$, then $w =$ _____ ÷ _____

$w =$ _____

So the width is _____ inches.

w	Perimeter = 30 in.

11 in.

Solving Perimeter and Area Problems

Use the formulas for perimeter and area of rectangles to solve each problem.

1. Find x.

x

2 ft | Area = 28 sq ft |

_____

2. Find y.

y | Perimeter = 86 in.

25 in.

_____

3. Find the length. Then find the perimeter.

3 ft | Area = 33 sq ft |

ℓ

_____

4. Find the width. Then find the area.

w | Perimeter = 40 in.

12 in.

_____

Michael designs and makes quilts. Answer questions **5–8** about the dimensions of his quilts. You may wish to use a sketch to help you solve the problem.

5. He made a baby quilt that was 3 feet wide. Its perimeter was 16 feet. What was its area?

_____

6. He made a queen-sized quilt that was 8 feet long. Its area was 64 square feet. What was its perimeter?

_____

7. Reason He wanted to make another quilt with an area of 42 square feet. What are its possible dimensions if they must be whole numbers? Which length and width makes the most sense for a quilt?

_____

_____

8. Persevere The perimeter of another quilt had to be 34 feet because he only had that much binding. If he wanted it to be 8 feet long, what would its area be?

A 18 sq ft   **B** 72 sq ft   **C** 144 sq ft   **D** 292 sq ft

Solving Measurement Problems

Lance has a 5-gallon aquarium. He fills the aquarium using a
2-quart container. How many times will he have to fill the 2-quart
container to fill the aquarium?

Use a bar diagram to see how the units are related.

1 gal			
1 qt	1 qt		

$4 \text{ qt} = 1 \text{ gal or } 2 \text{ qt} = \frac{1}{2} \text{ gal}$.

So, Lance has to fill the container 2 times to fill one gallon in the
aquarium.

Since there are 5 gallons, he must fill the container 2×5, or
10 times.

In **1–2**, use the diagram shown to help solve the problem.

1. It took Amber 5 hours 16 minutes to finish a race. Her time at
   the halfway marker was 2 hours 49 minutes. How long did it
   take Amber to complete the second half of the race?

5 h 16 min	
2 h 49 min	?

   1 h = _____ min, so 5 h 16 min = 4 h _____ min

   4 h 76 min − 2 h 49 min = _____

2. **Reason** Jeremy uses 18 inches of twine for each box he packs for shipping.
   How many yards of twine does he need to wrap 5 boxes?

Solving Measurement Problems

In **1**, use the diagram shown to help solve the problem.

1. Tawny has $2\frac{1}{2}$ pints of juice. She has juice glasses that hold 5 fluid ounces. How many glasses can she fill with juice?

In **2–5**, draw a diagram to help solve each problem.

2. **Reason** A race is 10 kilometers long. Markers will be placed at the beginning and end of the race-course and at each 500-meter mark. How many markers are needed to mark the course for the race?

3. On Monday, students at a summer camp spent 4 hours 25 minutes at the pool learning to swim. In the morning they spent 2 hours 48 minutes at the pool. How long did the students spend at the pool in the afternoon?

4. **Persevere** The mass of a tiger at a zoo is 135 kilograms. Randy's cat has a mass of 5,000 grams. How many times greater is the mass of the tiger than the mass of Randy's cat?

5. Lou cuts $2\frac{1}{3}$ yards of fabric from a 9-yard roll of fabric. Then he cuts 4 more feet of fabric from the roll. How much fabric is left on the roll?

   A $3\frac{2}{3}$ yd   **B** $5\frac{1}{3}$ yd   **C** $6\frac{1}{3}$ yd   **D** $6\frac{2}{3}$ yd

Solving Problems Involving Money

Christine buys a loaf of bread from the bakery that costs $3.59.
She pays for the loaf with a $5 bill. What is Christine's change?

First, start with the cost of the bread. Use coins and bills until you
reach the amount Christine paid.

$3.59 → $3.60 → $3.65 → $3.75 → $4.00 → $5.00

Second, count the change. Count coins and bills in reverse order.
$1.00 → $1.25 → $1.35 → $1.40 → $1.41

Christine's change is $1.41.

List the coins and bills you would use to make the amount of
change for each situation. Then tell the amount of change.

1. Bryce bought a map that cost $7.35. He used a $10 bill to pay
   for the map. What is his change?

   _____

2. Nora bought a pair of running shoes that cost $34.29. She
   paid for the shoes with two $20 bills. What is her change?

   _____

3. **Reason** Orlando bought some groceries that cost a total
   of $22.68. He used a $20 bill and a $10 bill to pay for the
   groceries. What are two different ways he could receive his
   change? What is his change?

   _____

   _____

Solving Problems Involving Money

Tell the amount of change for each situation.

1. Kyle bought a DVD that cost $19.23, including tax. She gave the sales clerk a $20 bill. How much change should Kyle receive?

_____

2. **Mental Math** Sean uses a $5 bill and two quarters to pay for a souvenir mug that costs $4.35. What is his change?

_____

3. Zooey bought a new skateboard that costs $36.79. How much change should she get if she paid for the skateboard with two $20-bills?

_____

4. **Reason** Vince buys a model train that costs $6.55. Why might he give the salesperson a $10 bill and a nickel? What is his change?

_____

5. **Critique Reasoning** Julia spent $7.36 on lunch. She gave the cashier two $5 bills to pay the bill and received $2.54 in change. Did she receive the correct change? Explain.

_____

6. **Reason** Brad paid for a book that cost $13.40 with a $20 bill. What is the least combination of coins and bills that can be used to make his change? What are two other different combinations of coins and bills that can be used to make the change?

_____

_____

7. Emma buys a game for $26.84. She pays for the game with a $20 bill and two $5 bills. How much change should she receive?

A $1.84   B $3.16   C $3.26   D $3.84

Solving Problems Involving Line Plots

Eight people in a class measured the length of their steps and got the following measurements: 1.6 feet, 1.8 feet, 1.9 feet, 1.7 feet, 1.9 feet, 1.8 feet, 1.8 feet, and 1.7 feet.

Draw a number line. Start with the least measurement and end with the greatest measurement.

```
←──┼────┼────┼────┼──→
   1.6  1.7  1.8  1.9
```

What is the most common step length?

What is the difference between the greatest step length and the least step length?

Add your data to the line plot. Use Xs to show each measurement. Give the line plot a title.

Length of Steps in Feet

```
                    X
          X    X    X
     X    X    X    X
←────┼────┼────┼────┼──→
    1.6  1.7  1.8  1.9
```

You can draw a line plot to find out.

The most common step length is 1.8 feet. The difference between the greatest step length and least step length is 0.3 feet.

For **1–3,** use the data set below which lists the number of books each student in Mr. Kent's class read in the last month.

$$2, 2\frac{1}{2}, 3\frac{1}{2}, 3, 4, 3\frac{1}{2}, 2, 3\frac{1}{2}, 4, 3\frac{1}{2}, 4\frac{1}{2}, 3\frac{1}{2}$$

1. Make a line plot of the data.

2. What is the most common number of books read in the last month?

   _____

3. **Use tools** What is the difference between the greatest and least number of books read?

   _____

Solving Problems Involving Line Plots

For **1–4,** use the data set below which lists the length of time in seconds it takes for each student in Ms. Sousa's class to say the alphabet.

$5, 4, 4\frac{1}{2}, 6, 5, 6\frac{1}{2}, 5\frac{1}{2}, 7, 5\frac{1}{2}, 7\frac{1}{2}, 6, 4\frac{1}{2}, 4\frac{1}{2}, 4\frac{1}{2}, 4, 6, 4\frac{1}{2}, 5\frac{1}{2}, 5, 6\frac{1}{2}$

1. Make a line plot of the data.

2. **Use Tools** What is the most common time it takes a student to say the alphabet?

_____

3. **Writing to Explain** Yuri says that the difference between the least amount of time it takes a student to say the alphabet and the greatest amount of time is $4\frac{1}{2}$ seconds. Do you agree? Explain.

_____

_____

4. **Reason** A new student joins Ms. Sousa's class. That student can say the alphabet in $3\frac{1}{2}$ seconds. What is the new difference between the greatest length of time and the least length of time?

A $4\frac{1}{2}$ seconds   **B** 4 seconds   **C** $3\frac{1}{2}$ seconds   **D** 3 seconds

Problem Solving:
Solve a Simpler Problem
and Make a Table

Squares A student is making a pattern of squares out of cotton balls. Each unit on a side of the pattern is made up of 2 cotton balls. How many cotton balls will the student need to make a pattern that is 4 units high and 4 units wide?

1 unit

Read and Understand

Step 1: What do you know?
There are 2 cotton balls in each unit. The square is 4 units high and 4 units wide.

Step 2: What are you trying to find?
How many cotton balls are needed in all.

Plan and Solve

Step 3: What strategy will you use?

Strategy: Solve a simpler problem.

Problem 1: How many cotton balls are needed for a 1-unit by 1-unit square?

8 cotton balls are needed for a 1-unit square.

Problem 2: How many cotton balls are needed for a 2-unit by 2-unit square?

16 cotton balls are needed for a 2-unit square.

There are 2 cotton balls for each unit on the side.
There are always 4 sides, so the pattern is the
number of units in each side, multiplied by 2 cotton balls, multiplied by 4 sides.

Square units	1×1	2×2	4×4
Cotton balls needed	8	16	32

Answer: 32 cotton balls are needed.

Look Back and Check

Step 4: Is your work correct?
Yes, all of my computations are correct, and I saw the correct pattern.

1. Joan works for 6 hr each weekday, and 8 hr total on the weekends. She earns $6 an hour on weekdays and $9 an hour on weekends. How much money does she earn each week?

_____

_____

Problem Solving: Solve a Simpler Problem and Make a Table

Sam needs to cut a piece of sheet metal into 8 pieces. It takes him 5 minutes to make each cut.

1. How many cuts will Sam make? _____

2. Writing to Explain How would making a table help you to find the number of minutes it took Sam to cut the sheet metal into 8 pieces?

_____

_____

3. How long will it take Sam to turn the sheet metal into 8 pieces? Write your answer in a complete sentence.

_____

Sarah is having a slumber party with her 11 friends and they are telling scary stories. They divide into 3 groups and each group tells a story. Each group member talks for 3 minutes.

4. How many people are in each group? _____

5. How many minutes does each group take to tell a story? _____

6. How many minutes does it take for all three groups to tell their stories? _____

7. If Sarah divided her friends into 4 groups and each person still got the same time to talk, how long would it take to tell the stories?

A 16 minutes   **B** 36 minutes   **C** 48 minutes   **D** 144 minutes

Points, Lines, and Planes

Here are some important geometric terms.

X
•

A   B

Point
A point is an exact
location in space.
This is point X.

Line
A line is a straight path
of points that goes on
and on in both directions.
This is line AB.

Parallel lines
Parallel lines
never intersect.

Intersecting lines
Intersecting lines
pass through the
same point.

Perpendicular lines
Perpendicular lines
form right angles.

Use geometric terms to describe what is shown. Be as specific as possible.

1.

_____

_____

2.

_____

_____

3.

_____

_____

4. Name three different lines.

_____

5. Name a set of parallel lines.

_____

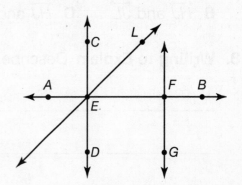

Name _____

Points, Lines, and Planes

Use geometric terms to describe what is shown. Be as specific as possible.

1.

_____

2.

_____

3.
X

_____

4.

_____

For **5–7,** use the diagrams to the right.

5. Name two lines.

_____

6. Name two lines that are perpendicular.

_____

7. Which two lines are parallel?

A $\overleftrightarrow{HK}$ and $\overleftrightarrow{JL}$ **C** $\overleftrightarrow{HJ}$ and $\overleftrightarrow{JK}$

B $\overleftrightarrow{HJ}$ and $\overleftrightarrow{JL}$ **D** $\overleftrightarrow{HJ}$ and $\overleftrightarrow{LM}$

8. Writing to Explain Describe a point.

_____

_____

Line Segments, Rays, and Angles

Here are some important geometric terms.

X   Y   A   B

Line segment
A line segment is part of a line. It has two endpoints. This is line segment $\overline{XY}$.

Ray
A ray is part of a line. It has one endpoint and goes on and on in one direction. This is ray $\overrightarrow{AB}$.

Right angle
A right angle is a square corner, or 90 degrees.

Obtuse angle
An obtuse angle is greater than a right angle.

Acute angle
An acute angle is less than a right angle.

Straight angle
A straight angle is 180 degrees.

Use geometric terms to describe what is shown. Be as specific as possible.

1.

2.

3.

_____   _____   _____

_____   _____   _____

4. Name three different rays.

_____

5. Name two different line segments.

_____

Line Segments, Rays, and Angles

Use geometric terms to describe what is shown. Be as specific as possible.

1.

_____

2.

_____

3.

_____

4.

_____

For **5–7**, use the diagrams to the right.

5. Name two line segments.

_____

6. Name two obtuse angles.

_____

7. Which is the geometric term for angle *HJK*?

   A Acute angle   **C** Right angle

   B Obtuse angle   **D** Straight angle

8. **Writing to Explain** Describe an acute angle.

_____

_____

Understanding Angles and Unit Angles

You can find the measure of an angle using fractions of a circle.

The angle is $\frac{1}{6}$ of a circle.

What is the measure of this angle?

Divide to find the angle measure of $\frac{1}{6}$ of a circle.

Remember, $\frac{1}{6}$ means 1 of 6 equal parts, so divide by 6 to find the angle measure.

Number of degrees
in whole circle ⟶ $360° ÷ 6 = 60°$ ⟵ Number of degrees in the angle.

The measure of this angle is ___60___ degrees.

For Exercise **1,** show the work you do to find the measure of the angle.

1. **Use Structure** A circle is divided into 9 equal parts.

   What is the measure of this angle?

   Write an equation using division to find the measure of the angle.

   _____ ÷ _____ = _____

   The measure of this angle is _____ degrees.

2. Janie cut a round slice of watermelon into 5 equal pieces. What is the angle of each piece? Use equivalent fractions.

   The measure of this angle is _____ degrees.

3. Frank cut a pie into 10 equal slices. There are only 3 slices left. What is the measure of the angle for the 3 slices that are left? _____.

4. Maria cut a pizza into 8 equal slices. She put a slice of pizza on 3 plates. What is the measure of the angle for the slices that are left? _____.

Understanding Angles and Unit Angles

In **1–3**, find the measure of each angle.

1. The angle is $\frac{1}{12}$ of the circle.

_____ degrees

2. A circle is divided into 20 equal parts. What is the angle measure of three of those parts?

_____ degrees

3. A circle is divided into 9 equal parts. What is the angle measure of two of those parts?

_____ degrees

4. Reasoning Kurt cut pizzas into wedges measuring 40 degrees. If each person eats one piece of pizza, how many people could he feed with two whole pizzas?

_____

5. Sam cut a pie into equal slices. There are only 3 slices left. The angle measure for the three slices is 72°. How many slices did Sam cut the pie into?

_____

6. Writing to Explain A circle is divided into 18 equal parts. How many degrees is the angle for each part? How many degrees is the angle for 5 parts? Explain.

_____

_____

7. Brian cut an extra large round pizza into 12 pieces. Seven of the pieces were eaten. What angle measure of pizza is left?

A 30°   **B** 120°   **C** 150°   **D** 210°

Measuring with Unit Angles

You can use an angle you know to find the measure of an angle
you do not know. Use the smaller angle of the beige pattern
block. It has a measure of 30°.

Find the measure of the angle below.

Two of the 30° angles will fit into the angle.

Add: 30° + 30° = 60°. The measure of this angle is 60°.

Use the beige pattern block to find the measure of the angle.
Draw lines to show how many 30° angles fit into the angle.

1.

_____

2. Be Precise Explain how you found the measure of the angle.

_____

_____

_____

_____

_____

Measuring with Unit Angles

In **1–5,** find the measure of each angle. Use pattern blocks to help.

1.

_____

2.

_____

3.

_____

4.

_____

5. What is the measure of this angle?

A 105°   **B** 120°   **C** 135°   **D** 150°

6. Communicate Explain how you found the measure of the
angle in Exercise 3. Use pictures, words, and numbers in
your explanation.

_____

_____

_____

_____

Measuring Angles

An angle is formed by two rays that meet at a common endpoint called the vertex. The angle is measured in **degrees (°)**.

An angle can be measured or created using a **protractor**.

To measure an angle:

Place the protractor's center on the vertex of the angle, and the 0° mark on one of the angle's rays. Read the number in degrees where the other ray of the angle crosses the protractor.

To create an angle:

Draw a dot to show the vertex of the angle. Place the center of the protractor on the vertex point. Draw another point at the 0° mark and another point at the angle degree mark. Draw rays from the vertex through the other points.

For Exercises **1** through **3**, measure the angles.

1.

_____

2.

_____

3.

_____

For Exercises **4** through **9**, draw the angles.

4. 65°

5. 90°

6. 145°

7. 75°

8. 135°

9. 180°

Measuring Angles

For Exercises **1** through **4**, use a protractor to measure the angle.

1. _____   2. _____   3. _____   4. _____

For Exercises **5** through **8**, draw the angle:

5. 45°   **6.** 150°   **7.** 60°   **8.** 180°

9. Rich has 3 pieces of pizza. Each pizza end forms a 20° angle.
   If all of the pieces were placed together what would the size
   of the angle be?

_____

10. Stuart, Sam, Sue, and Sally have equal-sized pieces of pie.
   When the 4 pieces are put together they form a 100° angle.
   What is the angle of each piece?

   A 100°   **B** 50°   **C** 25°   **D** 15°

11. Writing to Explain Gail and her 3 friends all share half a
   pie. Gail and her friends each eat an equal-sized piece.
   They believe each piece has an angle equal to 25°. Are their
   calculations correct? Explain.

_____

_____

_____

Adding and Subtracting Angle Measures

You can add to find angle measures.

$$x = 60 + 90 \qquad x = 150$$

You can subtract to find angle measures.

$$x = 180 - 120 \qquad x = 60$$

Angles *TUW* and *WUV*, together, make the larger angle, *TUV*. Add or subtract. Write the missing angle measure.

Angle Measure (°)

	∠*TUW*	∠*WUV*	∠*TUV*
1.	120	45	
2.	105		155
3.	100		170
4.		25	150
5.	112	36	

6. **Reason** Use the picture at the right. Jody is making a mosaic. She places two pieces along an edge as shown. She needs a third piece to fill the space between these two pieces. What size corner-angle does the third piece need to have in order to fill the space with no gaps?

_____

_____

Adding and Subtracting Angle Measures

Use the diagram. Add or subtract to find the angle measure.

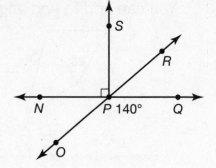

1. What is the measure of ∠NPO? _____

2. What is the measure of ∠SPR if the measure of ∠RPQ is 40°? _____

3. If a line segment PT is drawn dividing ∠SPN into two equal parts, what are the measures of the two smaller angles? _____

4. Use the diagram.

   a. Draw line segment PT so that it divides ∠OPQ into two smaller parts.

   b. What is the measure of the new angle ∠OPT you formed?

   _____

   c. Write an equation and solve it to find the measure of ∠TPQ.

   _____

   _____

5. ∠CMW and ∠WML together form ∠CML. ∠CMW is a right angle. What must be true about ∠CML?

   A It is an obtuse angle.

   B It is a straight angle.

   C Its measure is greater than 90°.

   D Its measure is greater than 180°.

6. **Writing to Explain** Use the diagram above. Shane sees that ∠OPN and ∠SPR are both smaller angles within ∠OPR, a straight angle. He says you can subtract the measure of ∠OPN from 180 to find the measure of ∠SPR. Is he right? Explain.

   _____

   _____

   _____

Name _____

Polygons

Polygons are closed plane figures that are made up of line segments. All of the line segments connect. All of the sides of a polygon are straight, not curved.

Polygon
Closed figure made of line segments.

Not a polygon
Not a closed figure.

Not a polygon
Not all of the sides are line segments.

Here are some common polygons. Note that the sides of polygons do not all have to be the same length.

Octagon
8 sides

Hexagon
6 sides

Pentagon
5 sides

Quadrilateral
4 sides

Triangle
3 sides

Draw an example of each type of polygon. How many sides and vertices does each one have?

1. Hexagon

_____

2. Quadrilateral

_____

3. Pentagon

_____

4. Octagon

_____

Polygons

Draw an example of each polygon. How many sides and vertices
does each one have?

1. Quadrilateral   **2.** Octagon   **3.** Hexagon

The map shows the shapes
of buildings in Polygon Park.
Identify the polygons that
are lettered.

4. A

_____

5. D

_____

6. C   **7.** B

_____   _____

8. E   **9.** F

_____   _____

10. Which is the point where sides meet in a polygon?

     A edge   **B** endpoint   **C** side   **D** vertex

11. **Writing to Explain** Describe two polygons by the number of
vertices and sides each has.

_____

Triangles

Equilateral triangle
All sides are the
same length.

Isosceles triangle
At least two sides
are the same length.

Scalene triangle
No sides are the
same length.

Right triangle
One angle is a
right angle.

Acute triangle
All three angles
are acute angles.

Obtuse triangle
One angle is an
obtuse angle.

Classify each triangle by its sides and then by its angles.

1.

_____

2.

_____

3.

_____

4.

_____

Triangles

Classify each triangle by its sides and then by its angles.

1.   _____

2.   _____

3.   _____

Write the name of each triangle.

4.   **5.**

_____   _____

6. Which is a triangle with one right angle?

    A Equilateral triangle **B** Obtuse triangle **C** Right triangle **D** Acute triangle

7. Writing to Explain Why can't a triangle have more than one obtuse angle?

_____

_____

_____

Quadrilaterals

Square
There are four
right angles. All
sides are the
same length.

Rectangle
There are four
right angles.

Parallelogram
Opposite sides
are parallel.

Rhombus
Opposite
sides are
parallel and all
sides are the
same length.

Trapezoid
There is only
one pair of
parallel sides.

Quadrilateral
A polygon with
4 sides.

Write the name of each quadrilateral.

1.

_____

2.

_____

3.

4.

Quadrilaterals

Write all the names you can use for each quadrilateral.

1.

_____

2.

_____

3.

_____

4.

_____

5.

_____

6. Which is **NOT** a quadrilateral?

A rhombus　　**B** rectangle　　**C** right triangle　　**D** trapezoid

7. Writing to Explain Explain why a square can never be
a trapezoid.

_____

_____

_____

Name _____

Line Symmetry

Symmetric figures are figures that can be folded to make two halves that match each other. The lines that divide a symmetric figure into matching parts are called lines of symmetry.

This square has 4 lines of symmetry. If you fold the square along any of the 4 dashed lines, the two halves will lie on top of each other.

Tell if each line is a line of symmetry.

1.

2.

3.

4.

_____   _____   _____   _____

Tell how many lines of symmetry each figure has.

5.

6.

7.

8.

_____   _____   _____   _____

9. **Reasoning** How many lines of symmetry does the letter R have?   _____

10. Complete the drawing so that the figure is symmetric.

Copyright © Pearson Education, Inc., or its affiliates. All Rights Reserved. 4

Line Symmetry

Tell if each line is a line of symmetry.

1.

_____

2.

_____

3.

_____

Tell how many lines of symmetry each figure has.

4.

_____

5.

_____

6.

_____

7. Draw lines of symmetry.

8. How many lines of symmetry does a rhombus that is not a square have?

A 0   B 1   C 2   D 3

9. **Writing to Explain** Explain why a square is always symmetric.

_____

_____

_____

Problem Solving:
Make and Test Generalizations

When you make a generalization, you make a broad statement about something that a group has in common. A generalization helps you find patterns. When you make a generalization, it is important to test it to be sure it is correct.

Example: $1 \times 24 = 24$ $1 \times 93 = 93$
$1 \times 126 = 126$

Generalization: A number multiplied by 1 is itself.

Test: If I multiply a different number by 1, it is also equal to itself. For example, $1 \times 2 = 2$; $1 \times 3 = 3$; $1 \times 4 = 4$, etc.; any number multiplied by 1 is itself. My generalization is correct.

In some cases, it is possible to find more than one correct generalization:

Example: Jessica found a red pencil, 3 red pens, and 2 red markers in her backpack.

Generalization #1: The things Jessica found are all writing instruments.

Generalization #2: The things Jessica found are all red.

Test: I can write with a pencil, a pen, and a marker. Also, the pencil, the pens, and the markers are all red. My generalizations are correct.

1. Randy has 2 tennis balls, 6 marbles, and 1 orange in his desk drawer. What generalization can you make about these things?

   _____

2. This week, Sandy was out sick on Monday and Tuesday. Last week, Jared was out sick on Thursday and Friday. The week before, Elisa was out sick on Wednesday and Thursday. What generalization can you make about these three students' absences? Can you make a second generalization?

   _____

3. Write down the first three multiples of 15, 20, and 25. What generalization can you make about all multiples of 5?

   _____

Problem Solving:
Make and Test Generalizations

For Exercises **1** through **3**, use the images to make a
generalization and test your answer.

1.

_____

_____

2.

_____

_____

3.

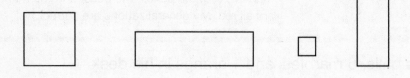

_____

_____

4. Which statement below is a good generalization about
   all polygons?

   A All polygons have right angles.

   B All polygons are closed figures.

   C All polygons have parallel sides.

   D All polygons are quadrilaterals.

5. **Writing to Explain** Try to draw a triangle with 2 right or
   obtuse angles. What generalizations can you make about
   the angles of a triangle? Explain.

   _____

   _____

Name _____

The Distributive Property

You can use the Distributive Property to multiply mentally.

Example A. Evaluate 7×53.

	7×53

Break 53 apart into $50 + 3$. $7 \times (50 + 3)$

Then distribute the 7 to each part. $(7 \times 50)\ 1\ (7 \times 3)$

Multiply. $350 + 21$

Add the products. 371

Example B. Evaluate $5(42) - 5(2)$. Remember $5(42)$ means 5×42.

Use the Distributive Property in reverse. $5(42) - 5(2)$

Join 42 and 2 using the minus sign. $5\ (42 - 2)$

Subtract. 5×40

Multiply the difference by 5. 200

Find each missing number.

1. $8 \times (30 + 2) = (8 \times \underline{\hspace{1cm}}) + (8 \times 2)$ **2.** $(6 \times \underline{\hspace{1cm}}) - (6 \times 7) = 6 \times (37 - 7)$

3. $8(28) = 8(20) + 8(\underline{\hspace{1cm}})$ **4.** $3(22) + 3(4) = 3(\underline{\hspace{1cm}}) + 3(6)$

Use the Distributive Property and mental math to evaluate.

5. $6(24)$ _____   **6.** $4(13) - 4(3)$ _____

7. $7(24 + 6)$ _____   **8.** $2(72)$ _____

9. $9(12) + 9(3)$_____   **10.** $5(24 - 3)$ _____

11. Number Sense What are two other ways to write $9(46)$?

_____

The Distributive Property

Find each missing number.

1. $8 \times (30 + 2) = (8 \times \underline{\hspace{2cm}}) + (8 \times 2)$ **2.** $8(94) = 8(\underline{\hspace{1.5cm}}) + 8(4)$

3. $5(45 + 5) = 5(\underline{\hspace{1.5cm}})$ **4.** $9(42) - 9(4) = 9(30) + 9(\underline{\hspace{1.5cm}})$

Use the Distributive Property and mental math to evaluate.

5. $3(58 - 8)$ _____   **6.** $7(31 + 19)$ _____

7. $9(72)$ _____   **8.** $4(26) - 4(16)$ _____

9. $8(41) + 8(5)$ _____   **10.** $5(22 - 5)$ _____

11. Describe the mental math steps you would use to find $7(42)$.

_____

_____

12. Number Sense Use mental math to evaluate the expression $6(31) + 6(4) - 6(15)$.

_____

13. Geometry Write an expression for the area of this rectangle. Evaluate your expression to find the area.

20 cm   4 cm

8 cm

_____

14. Algebra Which expression is equal to $12m + 12n$?

   A $12mn$

   B $12m + n$

   C $12m - 12n$

   D $12(m + n)$

Using Variables to Write Expressions

A variable represents a quantity that can change. To use a variable to write an algebraic expression, you need to decide which operation is appropriate. To help you, some words and phrases are listed below.

Word phrase	Variable	Operation	Algebraic Expression
ten **more than** a number b	b	Addition	$b + 10$
the **sum** of 8 and a number c	c		$8 + c$
five **less than** a number d	d	Subtraction	$d - 5$
15 **decreased by** a number e	e		$15 - e$
the **product** of 8 and a number f	f	Multiplication	$8f$
19 **times** a number g	g		$19g$
the quotient of a number h **divided by** 2	h	Division	$h \div 2$
a number i **divided into** 50	i		$50 \div i$

Write each algebraic expression.

1. a number m **divided by** 6 _____

2. the **sum** of 4 and a number n _____   **3.** 4 **times** a number p _____

4. a number n **divided into** 7 _____   **5.** 3 **less than** a number r _____

6. a fewer grapes than 12 _____   **7.** q sandwiches at \$8 each _____

8. Each fourth grader has 5 notebooks. Write an algebraic expression to represent the number of notebooks the entire class has.

Identify the operation. _____   Write the expression. _____

9. **Writing to Explain** Write an algebraic expression to represent the situation below. Explain how the expression relates to the situation.

Some monkeys share 7 bananas equally among themselves.

_____

_____

Name _____

Using Variables to Write Expressions

Write each algebraic expression.

1. 4 more than a number *b* _____
2. twice a number *a* _____

3. 20 less than a number *c* _____
4. the product of 5 and a number *d* _____

5. 30 divided by a number *f* _____
6. the sum of a number *e* and 3 _____

7. 9 more stripes than a number *h* _____

8. 14 fewer hats than five times a number *i* _____

9. Chad has $80. He buys a book. Which expression shows how much money Chad has left?

    A $s + 80$

    B $80 - s$

    C $80s$

    D $s \div 80$

10. A coffee shop has booths and counter seating. Each booth can seat 4 people. Another 20 people can sit at the counter. Which expression shows how many customers can be seated in the coffee shop?

    A $20b - 4$ B $20b + 4$ C $4b - 20$ D $4b + 20$

11. Sofia bought some flats of daisies. Each flat holds 9 daisies. Sofia has planted 10 daisies. Is $9x + 10$ a reasonable way to represent the number of daisies that Sofia has left to plant? Explain your answer.

    _____

    _____

    _____

Name _____

Using Patterns to Divide

You can use basic facts and patterns to divide mentally.

Using basic facts	Using patterns
What is 140 ÷ 70?	What is 4,200 ÷ 70?
Think: **140 ÷ 70** is the same as **14** tens ÷ 7 tens.	4,200 ÷ 70 is the same as 420 ÷ 7.
14 ÷ 7 = 2	Think: 42 ÷ 7 = 6, so 420 ÷ 7 = 60.
So, 140 ÷ 70 = 2.	So, 4,200 ÷ 70 = 60.

Find each quotient. Use mental math.

1. 210 ÷ 70 = _____

2. 360 ÷ 30 = _____

3. 400 ÷ 80 = _____

4. 1,200 ÷ 60 = _____

5. 4,000 ÷ 40 = _____

6. 4,800 ÷ 80 = _____

7. 2,700 ÷ 30 = _____

8. 3,500 ÷ 50 = _____

9. Number Sense How is dividing 140 by 20 the same as dividing 1,400 by 200?

_____

_____

_____

10. Writing to Explain Explain how you can use mental math to determine that 28,000 ÷ 70 = 400.

_____

_____

_____

Using Patterns to Divide

In **1** through **4**, find each quotient. Use mental math.

1. $160 \div 40 = 16$ tens $\div 4$ tens = _____

2. $6,300 \div 70 = 630$ tens $\div 7$ tens = _____

3. $140 \div 70 = 14$ tens $\div 7$ tens = _____

4. $3,700 \div 10 = 370$ tens $\div 1$ ten = _____

Use mental math to answer the following questions.

5. If the cans are divided evenly among the shelves, how many cans are on each shelf?

_____

Supermarket Storage	
Cans for sale	1,200
Shelves of cans	10
Rows per shelf	6

6. If the cans are divided evenly among the rows on each shelf, how many cans are in each row?

_____

7. Estimation Suppose there are 387 balls in the gym. If each bin can hold 48 balls, estimate the number of bins that will be needed to hold all the balls.

_____

_____

8. Algebra If $300,000 \div h = 6$, what is the value of h?

A 50   **B** 500   **C** 5,000   **D** 50,000

9. Solve the equation $n \div 50 = 5,000$. Explain your solution.

_____

_____

Name _____

Connecting Decimal and Whole Number Numeration

Whole number place values and decimal place values are shown below.
Each place value to the left is ten times as much as the place value
to its right.

Thousands	Hundreds	Tens	Ones	Decimal	Tenths	Hundredths	Thousandths
1,000	**100**	**10**	**1**	**.**	$0.1 = \frac{1}{10}$	$0.01 = \frac{1}{100}$	$0.001 = \frac{1}{1,000}$

For example, 1 ten is equal to 10 ones.   In 1 tenth, there are 10 hundredths.

Write the place value for the underlined digit. Then write the total
value of the underlined digit.

1. 348.<u>6</u>05

place value: _____

total value: _____

2. <u>2</u>,348.56

place value: _____

total value: _____

3. 449.65<u>4</u>

place value: _____

total value: _____

4. 3<u>4</u>8.56

place value: _____

total value: _____

5. Number Sense Does 6 have a greater value in 13.6 or in 83.06? Explain.

_____

_____

6. Writing to Explain Cassie ran one lap around the indoor track in 32.09 seconds.
She ran a second lap in 32.1 seconds. Did it take more or less time for Cassie to
run the second lap? Explain.

_____

Connecting Decimal and Whole Number Numeration

Write the place value for the underlined digit.

1. 5,009.94<u>1</u>

_____

2. 456.<u>9</u>6

_____

3. 3,116.<u>8</u>52

_____

4. 2,440.50<u>4</u>

_____

5. 599.0<u>4</u>

_____

6. 387.5<u>6</u>9

_____

7. <u>6</u>98.07

_____

8. <u>4</u>,456.87

_____

9. 9<u>8</u>6.54

_____

10. Which decimal has the same digit in the hundredths place and the hundreds place?

   A 145.54   **C** 965.439

   B 783.38   **D** 5,486.649

11. Donna bought 4.356 pounds of cheese. What is the value of each of the digits in 4.356?

_____

_____

_____

_____

12. Which is equal to 30 hundredths?

   A 3 thousandths **C** 3 tens

   B 3 tenths   **D** 3 thousands

13. Bill's average speed in the bicycle race was 29.215 miles per hour. What is the place value of the 1 in that number?

_____

14. Kathy has 2 tenths of a dollar. Tom has 10 hundredths of a dollar. Is Kathy's amount or is Tom's amount more?

_____

_____

Name _____

Rounding Decimals

You can use the number line below to help you round 7.14 to the nearest whole number. Is 7.14 closer to 7 or 8?

7.14 is less than halfway to 8. So, 7.14 is closer to 7.

A number line can help you round 8.762 to the nearest tenth.
Is 8.762 closer to 8.7 or 8.8?

8.762 is more than halfway to 8.8. So, 8.762 is closer to 8.8.

Round each number to the place of the underlined digit.

1. 0.<u>7</u>234

2. <u>4</u>.526

_____

_____

3. 3.86<u>2</u>9

4. 25.<u>1</u>47

_____

_____

For **5** and **6**, use the table at the right.

5. Round the number of inches of precipitation in Tallahassee to the nearest tenth.

Inches of Precipitation in 2007	
Daytona	45.02
Tallahassee	44.47
Orlando	38.49

_____

6. Round the number of inches of precipitation in Orlando to the nearest whole number.

7. **Number Sense** Marc earned $8.76 per hour working at the library. Round his wage to the nearest ten cents.

_____

_____

Rounding Decimals

Round each number to the place of the underlined digit.

1. 17.2̲3   _____

2. 56̲9.1   _____

3. 2.17̲85   _____

4. 26.0̲62   _____

5. **Reasoning** Name two different numbers that round to 9.2 when rounded to the nearest tenth.

_____

In early 2007, a U.S. dollar was equivalent to about 0.51 British pounds and about 1.17 Canadian dollars. Round each country's U.S. dollar equivalent to the nearest tenth of a dollar.

6. Britain   _____

7. Canada   _____

In 2007, the price of wheat was $10.03 per bushel. The price of soybeans was $11.93 per bushel. Round the price per bushel of wheat and soybeans to the nearest whole dollar.

8. wheat   _____

9. soybeans   _____

10. **Number Sense** Which number rounds to 600 when rounded to the nearest whole number?

   A 600.83   B 599.1   C 600.5   D 599.72

11. Write a definition of rounding in your own words.

_____

_____

Estimating Quotients with 2-Digit Divisors

You can use compatible numbers to estimate a quotient.

Estimate 228 ÷ 19.

Step 1: Find compatible numbers for 228 and 19.

Think: 20 can be divided evenly by 2.

200 is close to 228 and 20 is close to 19.

200 and 20 are compatible numbers.

Step 2: Divide. Use patterns to help you, if possible.

Think: 200 ÷ 20 is the same as 20 tens ÷ 2 tens.

20 ÷ 2 = 10
So, 200 ÷ 20 = 10.

Estimate each quotient using compatible numbers.

1. 540 ÷ 91   _____

2. 2,777 ÷ 74   _____

3. 29,952 ÷ 98   _____

4. 288 ÷ 37   _____

5. 1,784 ÷ 32   _____

6. 6,127 ÷ 32   _____

At Cambridge Elementary School, fourth-grade students are saving money for a summer trip to a theme park.

7. The amount Aubrey has saved is about how many times as great as the amount Joe has saved?

_____

_____

Student	Amount Saved
Rebecca	$110
Joe	$ 92
Ken	$225
Atiyah	$ 53
Aubrey	$189

Name _____

Estimating Quotients with 2-Digit Divisors

In **1** through **4**, estimate the quotients using compatible numbers.

1. 198 ÷ 41 = _____

2. 202 ÷ 52 = _____

3. 1,745 ÷ 63 = _____

4. 7,810 ÷ 22 = _____

5. Reasoning How do you know that 8,100 and 90 are NOT the best compatible numbers to use when estimating the quotient of 9,269 ÷ 88?

_____

_____

_____

6. Suppose there are 18 children at Georgi's party. Georgi's dad has 59 balloons and hands them out to the children. Estimate the number of balloons each child will receive.   _____

7. At a department store, a package of 8 t-shirts costs $38. Estimate how much each t-shirt costs.   _____

8. Number Sense Which is the closest estimate for 1,219 ÷ 44?

A 3   **B** 13   **C** 30   **D** 300

9. Explain how to estimate 425 ÷ 8.

_____

_____

_____

Name _____

Modeling Addition and Subtraction of Decimals

Adding decimals using a hundredths grid:

Add 0.26 + 0.12.

Step 1: Shade 26 squares to show 0.26.

Step 2: Use a different color. Shade 12 squares to show 0.12.

Step 3: Count all the squares that are shaded. How many hundredths are shaded in all? Write the decimal for the total shaded squares: 0.38.

So, 0.26 + 0.12 = 0.38.

Subtracting decimals using a hundredths grid:

Subtract 0.52 − 0.33.

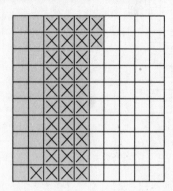

Step 1: Shade 52 squares to show 0.52.

Step 2: Cross out 33 squares to show 0.33.

Step 3: Count the squares that are shaded but not crossed out. Write the decimal: 0.19.

So, 0.52 − 0.33 = 0.19.

Add or subtract. You may use hundredths grids to help.

1. 0.42 + 0.37 = _____

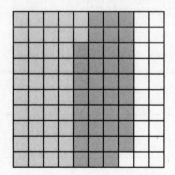

2. 0.37 − 0.31 = _____

Name _____

Modeling Addition and Subtraction of Decimals

Add or subtract. Use hundredths grids if necessary.

1. $0.24 + 0.53 =$ _____

2. $0.24 - 0.18 =$ _____

3. $0.88 + 0.25 =$ _____

4. $2.36 + 0.85 =$ _____

5. $0.61 - 0.47 =$ _____

6. $1.20 - 0.53 =$ _____

7. $2.20 - 1.97 =$ _____

8. $0.52 + 0.89 =$ _____

9. Number Sense Is the difference of
$2.45 - 1.54$ less than or greater than 1? _____

10. A jar of oregano holds 0.9 ounce. A jar of cayenne pepper
holds 0.75 ounce. How much more does a jar of oregano
hold? _____

11. Add: $1.75 + 1.29$

A 2.04   **B** 2.94   **C** 3.04   **D** 3.14

12. Explain how to use hundredths grids to
find $1.86 - 0.75$.

_____

_____

_____

Name _____

Relating Division to Multiplication of Fractions

How can you divide by a fraction?

Dividing a whole number by a fraction

$2 \div \dfrac{1}{3}$	Think: How can I divide two into one-thirds?
1. Two is the sum of one plus one. **2.** Each one is the sum of three one-thirds. **3.** Count the number of one-thirds. **Check** To divide a whole number by a fraction, multiply the whole number by the reciprocal of the fraction.	$2 \;=\; 1 \;+\; 1$ $\dfrac{1}{3}+\dfrac{1}{3}+\dfrac{1}{3} \;+\; \dfrac{1}{3}+\dfrac{1}{3}+\dfrac{1}{3}$ **6** $2 \div \dfrac{1}{3} = 2 \times \dfrac{3}{1} = \dfrac{2}{1} \times \dfrac{3}{1} = \dfrac{6}{1} = 6$

$3 \div \dfrac{3}{4}$	Think: How can I divide three into three-fourths?
1. Three is the sum of one plus one plus one. **2.** Each one is the sum of one three-fourths and one one-fourth. **3.** Count the number of three-fourths. **Check** Multiply the whole number by the reciprocal of the fraction.	$3 = 1 \;+\; 1 \;+\; 1$ $\dfrac{3}{4}+\dfrac{1}{4} \;+\; \dfrac{3}{4}+\dfrac{1}{4} \;+\; \dfrac{3}{4}+\dfrac{1}{4}$ $\dfrac{3}{4}+\dfrac{3}{4}+\dfrac{3}{4} \;+\; \dfrac{1}{4}+\dfrac{1}{4}+\dfrac{1}{4}$ $\dfrac{3}{4}+\dfrac{3}{4}+\dfrac{3}{4} \;+\; \dfrac{3}{4}$ **4** $3 \div \dfrac{3}{4} = 3 \times \dfrac{4}{3} = \dfrac{3}{1} \times \dfrac{4}{3} = \dfrac{12}{3} = 4$

Draw a picture that shows each division and write the answer.

1. $2 \div \dfrac{1}{2}$ _____

2. $2 \div \dfrac{2}{3}$ _____

Name _____

Relating Division to Multiplication of Fractions

In **1** and **2**, use the picture to find each quotient.

1. How many thirds are in 1?

_____

2. How many thirds are in 7?

_____

In **3** and **4**, draw a picture to find each quotient.

3. $3 \div \frac{1}{2}$

4. $4 \div \frac{1}{8}$

_____

_____

In **5** and **6**, use multiplication to find each quotient.

5. $6 \div \frac{1}{3}$

6. $5 \div \frac{1}{10}$

_____

_____

7. Julie bought 3 yards of cloth to make holiday napkin rings. If she needs $\frac{3}{4}$ of a yard to make each ring, how many rings can she make?

_____

8. When you divide a whole number by a fraction with a numerator of 1, explain how you can find the quotient.

_____

_____

_____

Multiplying Fractions and Whole Numbers

You can find the product of a fraction and a whole number.

Francesco needs $\frac{2}{3}$ yard of fabric to sew a shirt. How many yards of fabric will Francesco need to sew 6 shirts?

Step 1: Multiply the numerator by the whole number.

$2 \times 6 = 12$

Step 2: Place the product over the denominator. Simplify if possible.

$\frac{12}{3} = 4$ yards of fabric

Remember: In word problems, "of" often means "multiply."

Example: $\frac{3}{5}$ of $15 = \frac{3}{5} \times 15$

In **1** through **4**, find each product. Simplify if possible.

1. $\frac{2}{3} \times 30 =$ _____

2. $\frac{3}{4}$ of $28 =$ _____

3. $\frac{7}{8} \times 32 =$ _____

4. $\frac{3}{7}$ of $35 =$ _____

For Exercises **5** through **7**, use the table to the right.

5. What is $\frac{2}{7}$ the speed of a cheetah? _____

6. What is $\frac{1}{5}$ the speed of a lion? _____

7. What is $\frac{1}{5}$ the speed of a rabbit? _____

Animal	Speed (in mi/h)
Lion	50
Cheetah	70
Rabbit	35

Multiplying Fractions and Whole Numbers

Find each product.

1. $\frac{1}{2}$ of 96 = _____

2. $\frac{3}{7}$ of 28 = _____

3. $\frac{3}{4} \times 36 =$ _____

4. $45 \times \frac{4}{9} =$ _____

5. $56 \times \frac{7}{8} =$ _____

6. $42 \times \frac{3}{7} =$ _____

7. $\frac{1}{2}$ of 76 = _____

8. $\frac{3}{8}$ of 56 = _____

9. $\frac{1}{10} \times 200 =$ _____

10. $84 \times \frac{1}{4} =$ _____

11. $64 \times \frac{5}{8}$ _____

12. $20 \times \frac{11}{20} =$ _____

13. $\frac{3}{8}$ of 48 = _____

14. $\frac{1}{6}$ of 66 = _____

15. $\frac{4}{5} \times 30 =$ _____

16. $42 \times \frac{3}{6} =$ _____

17. $72 \times \frac{5}{8} =$ _____

18. $18 \times \frac{1}{3} =$ _____

19. $\frac{5}{6} \times 66 =$ _____

20. $\frac{11}{12} \times 72 =$ _____

21. $\frac{6}{7} \times 35 =$ _____

22. Complete the table by writing the product of each expression in the box below it. Use a pattern to find each product. Explain the pattern.

$\frac{1}{2} \times 64$	$\frac{1}{4} \times 64$	$\frac{1}{8} \times 64$	$\frac{1}{16} \times 64$

_____

23. **Reasoning** If $\frac{1}{3}$ of 1 is $\frac{1}{3}$, what is $\frac{1}{3}$ of 2, 3, and 4? _____

24. Which is $\frac{1}{3}$ of 225?

   A 75   **B** 113   **C** 150   **D** 450

25. Explain why $\frac{1}{4}$ of 4 equals one whole.

_____

_____

Name _____

Volume

Volume is a measure of the space inside a solid figure. It is measured in cubic units. A **cubic unit** is the volume of a cube which has edges that are 1 unit.

How to find the volume of a rectangular prism:

Counting unit cubes

Count the cubes in each layer: 8 cubes.

Multiply by the number of layers.

    8 cubes × 3 = 24 cubes

The volume of each cube is 1 cm^3.

The volume of the prism is 24 cm^3.

Using a formula

You know the length, l, the width, w, and the height, h. Calculate the volume, V, using the formula $V = l \times w \times h$.

$V = 2$ cm $\times 4$ cm $\times 3$ cm

$V = 24$ cm^3

Find the volume of each rectangular prism.

1.

_____

2.

_____

3.

10 in.

5 in.

2 in.

_____

Volume

Find the volume of each rectangular prism.

1. base area 36 in², height 5 in. _____

2. base area 52 cm², height 10 cm _____

3. base area 44 m², height 6 m _____

4.

5.

_____   _____

6. **Algebra** What is the height of a solid with a volume of 150 m³ and base area of 50 m²?   _____

Michael bought some cereal at the grocery store.

7. What is the base area of the box?

_____

8. What is the volume of the box?

_____

9. What is the base area of this figure?

   A 4.6 m²   **C** 460 m²

   B 46 m²   **D** 4,600 m²

10. Explain how you would find the base area of a rectangular prism if you know the volume and the height.

_____

Common Core
Standards Practice

Grade 4

Grade 4 Contents

 Standards Practice

 Assessment

Name _____

Common Core Georgia Performance Standards Practice

MCC4.OA.2 Multiply or divide to solve word problems involving multiplicative comparison, e.g., by using drawings and equations with a symbol for the unknown number to represent the problem, distinguishing multiplicative comparison from additive comparison.

1. This year, the music school has 85 students. Last year it had 17 students. How many times greater is this year's number of students?

   a. Write an equation for *f*.

   b. Solve the equation you wrote.

2. Jennifer bought 12 postcards at a yard sale. Frieda bought 8 times as many postcards.

   a. Write an equation that can be used to find *n*, the number of postcards that Frieda bought.

   b. Solve the equation you wrote.

3. At the apple orchard, Lisa picks 75 apples. Lisa picks 5 times more apples than Sharon picks.

   a. Write an equation that can be solved for *a*, the number of apples that Sharon picks.

   b. Solve the equation you wrote.

4. Janice uses 6 markers for an art project. Ivan uses 4 times as many markers as Janice.

    a. Write an equation to show the number of markers *m* that Ivan uses.

    b. Draw a model to illustrate the equation you wrote.

    c. Solve the equation you wrote.

5. Al sold 19 tickets to the school orchestra concert. Judy sold 3 more tickets than Al. Maria sold 3 times as many tickets as Al.

    a. What operations must you use to find out how many tickets Maria sold? Explain.

    b. Write an expression that you can use to find the number of tickets that Judy sold.

    c. How many tickets did Judy sell?

    d. Write an expression that you can use to find the number of tickets that Maria sold.

    e. How many tickets did Maria sell?

Name _____

Common Core Georgia Performance Standards Practice

MCC4.OA.3 Solve multistep word problems posed with whole numbers and having whole-number answers us   e four operations, including problems in which remainders must be interpreted. Represent these problems using   ons with a letter standing for the unknown quantity. Assess the reasonableness of answers using mental computatio estimation strategies including rounding.

1. George brought $94 to the shopping mall. He used the money to buy a sh   for $25, a pair of pants for $42, and 2 pairs of socks that each cost $6.

   How much money did George have after he finished shopping at the mall?

2. Nancy chopped the vegetables shown in the table, then mixed them into a salad. She divided the salad equally into 5 containers.

Broccoli	2 cups
Cauliflower	1 cup
Green peppers	2 cups
Red peppers	1 cup
Cucumbers	3 cups
Lettuce	6 cups

   How many cups of vegetables did Nancy put in each container?

3. At the school carnival, students sold 483 hamburgers for $4 each and 214 hot dog for $2 each.

   a. Write an equation to find how much money they took in from the sale of hamburgers. Use the letter *h* to represent the unknown amount. Then solve the equation.

   b. Write an equation to find how much money they took in from the sale of hot dogs. Use the letter *d* to represent the unknown amount. Then solve the equation.

   c. How much money did they take in from the hamburgers and hot dogs?

CC 5

4. The Walters family bought 3 ham sandwiches and 4 fruit cups for lunch. Each sandwich cost $4 and each fruit cup cost $2. How much did the family spend on lunch?

5. Volunteers at the park will plant 150 marigold plants and 60 petunia plants. They will plant 5 rows of petunias and twice as many rows of marigolds.

    a. How many rows of marigolds will the volunteers plant?

    b. How many petunias will they plant in each row?

6. Mr. Chen wants to buy 27 blue pens and 35 red pens. The pens are sold in packages of 8.

    a. How many packages of blue pens must he buy? Write an equation using the letter *b* for the unknown amount. Then solve the equation.

    b. How many packages of red pens will Mr. Chen buy? Write an equation and use the letter *r* for the unknown amount. Then solve the equation.

    c. One package of pens costs $2. How much will Mr. Chen spend on pens?

Name _____

Common Core Georgia Performance Standards Practice

MCC4.OA.4 Find all factor pairs for a whole number in the range 1–100. Recognize that a whole number is a multiple of each of its factors. Determine whether a given whole number in the range 1–100 is a multiple of a given one-digit number. Determine whether a given whole number in the range 1–100 is prime or composite.

1. Which of these are prime numbers? Circle all of the numbers that are prime.

17	37	38
45	57	59
63	84	89

2. Which of these numbers are composite? Circle all of the numbers that are composite.

2	5	9
19	33	45
53	69	91

3. Which of these numbers is a multiple of 8? Circle all of the numbers that are multiples of 8.

2	3	4
16	20	32
36	48	54
56	68	

4. Which set of numbers are all factors of 50?

A 1, 2, 5, 10, 25, 50
B 1, 2, 8, 12, 24, 50
C 1, 4, 5, 10, 12, 50
D 1, 4, 5, 9, 10, 50

5. Is 39 a prime or composite number? Explain how you know.

6. List four multiples of 9.

CC7

7. Which of these numbers are prime? Which are composite? Put an X on the prime numbers. Circle the composite numbers. In the space below, write the factors of each number that you identified as composite.

3	13	23
33	43	53
63	73	
83	93	

8. Write all of the factor pairs for 28.

9. The number 36 is a multiple of several numbers. List all of them.

10. What is the only even prime number? Explain how you know.

11. Answer each question. Explain how you know.

Is 81 a multiple of 3?

Is 46 a multiple of 4?

Is 55 a multiple of 7?

Is 72 a multiple of 9?

Is 45 a multiple of 6?

Name _____

Common Core Georgia Performance Standards Practice

MCC4.OA.5 Generate a number or shape pattern that follows a given rule. Identify apparent features of the pattern that were not explicit in the rule itself.

1. Continue the pattern below. Use the rule, "Add 4."

   4, _____, _____, _____, _____, _____

   What do you notice about the digits in the ones place?

2. Draw shapes to continue the pattern. Use the rule, "Add one side to the shape."

   , _____, _____

3. Continue the pattern below. Use the rule, "Divide by 2."

   96, _____, _____, _____, _____, _____

4. **a.** Continue the pattern below. Use the rule, "Move the dot around the square."

   b. Look closely. What pattern do you see that is not mentioned in the rule?

CC 9

5. a. Complete the number sequence below by using the rule, "Subtract 5."

50, _____, _____, _____, _____, _____, _____

b. What do you notice about the digits in the ones place?

6. a. Complete the number sequence below by using the rule, "Add 2."

3, _____, _____, _____, _____, _____, _____

b. What do you notice about the numbers in the pattern?

7. Complete the pattern by using the rule, "Add a dot to the square."

_____, _____, _____, _____

Name _____

Common Core Georgia Performance Standards Practice

MCC4.NBT.1 Recognize that in a multi-digit whole number, a digit in one place represents ten times what it represents in the place to its right.

1. Jonah wrote a 5-digit number on a piece of paper. He gave his friend Marbey these clues to find the number.

   a. The 4 is in the place that is ten times greater than the place where the 2 is.

   b. The 2 is in the place that is one hundred times less than the place where the 5 is.

   c. The 6 is in the place that is ten times less than the place where the 2 is.

   d. The 1 is in the place that is ten times greater than the place where the 5 is.

   What is the number?

3. Look at the number below.

   75,575

   a. How many times does the digit 5 appear in the number?

   b. How do the values of the digit 5 differ in the number?

   c. How much greater is the value of the first 5 compared to the value of the second 5?

   d. How much greater is the value of the second 5 compared to the value of the third 5?

2. Which of these statements is true about the number shown.

   169,961

   A The first 9 represents a value ten times greater than the second 9.

   B The first 9 represents a value one hundred times greater than the second 9.

   C The first 6 represents a value ten times greater than the second 6.

   D The first 6 represents a value one hundred times greater than the second 6.

4. Which of these statements is true about the number shown?

78,409

A The 7 represents a value that is 10 times greater than the 4.

B The 4 represents a value that is 10 times greater than the 9.

C The 8 represents a value that is 10 times greater than the 4.

D The 8 represents a value that is 2 times greater than the 4.

5. Minah gives the following clues about a 5-digit number.

a. The 8 is in a place that is 100 times greater than the place of the 2.

b. The 2 is in a place that is 100 times greater than the place of the 0.

c. The 3 is in a place that is 10 times less than the place of the 8.

d. The 5 is in a place that is 100 times less than the place of the 3.

What is the number?

6. Look at the number below.

38,108

a. How many times does the digit 8 appear in the number?

b. How do the values of the digit 8 differ in the number?

c. How much greater is the value of the first 8 compared to the value of the second 8?

d. Write a number with the same digits, but make the place of the first 8 be 10 times the place of the second 8.

Name _____

Common Core Georgia Performance Standards Practice

MCC4.NBT.2 Read and write multi-digit whole numbers using base-ten numerals, number names, and expanded form. Compare two multi-digit numbers based on meanings of the digits in each place, using >, =, and < symbols to record the results of comparisons.

1. What is 3,106 in expanded form?

   A 3,000 + 100 + 6
   B 3,000 + 10 + 6
   C 3,000 + 6
   D 3,000 + 100 + 60

2. Thirty-five thousand, four hundred seventeen people attended a county fair. What is this number in standard form?

   A 35,174
   B 35,417
   C 35,470
   D 35,471

3. What is 9,000 + 800 + 30 + 1 in standard form?

   A 9,031
   B 9,138
   C 9,381
   D 9,831

4. Which symbol should replace the circle to make the number sentence true?

   438 ◯ 400 + 30 + 8

   A <
   B ≠
   C =
   D >

5. Write 4,230 in expanded form.

6. Write a number sentence to compare 89,723 and 89,372. Use the < symbol.

   Explain how you know which number is greater.

7. A group of 246 people attend the school play. Write this number in words.

8. Write twenty-seven thousand, six hundred twelve in expanded form.

9. Dali sold one hundred fourteen tickets for the fundraiser. Sharon sold 141. Who sold more tickets? Write a number sentence to show your answer.

10. Write 3,406 in words and in expanded form.

11. Write a number sentence that compares 58,219 and 58,231.

Explain how you knew which symbol to use.

12. What symbol should replace the circle to make the number sentence true?

1,998 ◯ two thousand fourteen

Explain how you knew which symbol to use.

Name _____

Common Core Georgia Performance Standards Practice

MCC4.NBT.3 Use place value understanding to round multi-digit whole numbers to any place.

1. What is 192 rounded to the nearest ten?

   A 100
   B 180
   C 190
   D 200

2. Which number rounds to 5,600 when it is rounded to the nearest hundred?

   A 5,674
   B 5,637
   C 5,549
   D 5,512

3. The school talent show raised $2,914. What is this amount rounded to the nearest thousand and to the nearest hundred?

4. What is 6,708 rounded to the nearest ten?

5. On Thursday, 45 students walked to school. What is this number rounded to the nearest ten?

6. Aisha thinks that 1,275 rounded to the nearest hundred is 1,200 because "2 is less than 5."

   a. What might be Aisha's misunderstanding about rounding?

   b. Help Aisha correct her misunderstanding by explaining rounding.

7. The population of Centerville is 89,582. What is the population rounded to the nearest thousand?

A 90,000

B 89,600

C 89,500

D 89,000

8. Write a number that would round to 5,000 when it is rounded to the nearest thousand.

9. The attendance at an amusement park during the month of July was 174,383. What is the attendance rounded to the nearest thousand?

10. A newspaper reported that about 27,000 people attended a major league baseball game. If the actual attendance was rounded to the nearest thousand, how many people could have attended the game?

A 27,942

B 27,610

C 26,789

D 26,495

11. Write two numbers that round to 150 when they are rounded to the nearest ten.

12. Ken says that 9,138 rounded to the nearest thousand is 9,100 because "3 is less than 5."

a. What might be Ken's misunderstanding about rounding?

b. Help Ken correct his misunderstanding.

Name _____

Common Core Georgia Performance Standards Practice

MCC4.NBT.4 Fluently add and subtract multi-digit whole numbers using the standard algorithm.

1. Use the information in the table to answer each question below.

City	Population (2010)
Gulfport, MS	67,793
Redlands, CO	8,685
Rocky River, OH	20,213

a. In 2000, the population of Gulfport, MS, was 71,127. How many more people lived in Gulfport, MS, in 2000 than in 2010?

b. In 2010, how many more people lived in Rocky River, OH, than in Redlands, CO?

c. In 2010, what was the total population of the three cities listed in the table?

2. Find the sum.

    4,068
+ 2,291
———————

3. Find the difference.

   500,000
− 184,875
———————

4. Students at the Lincoln Elementary School are selling tickets to the school spring fair. The third graders have sold 1,673 tickets. The fourth graders have sold 3,098 tickets. What is the total number of tickets the students in both classes have sold?

A 1,425

B 4,671

C 4,771

D 5,771

5. A cowgirl spends $995 on a used trail saddle. She also spends $360 on new saddlebags. How much does she spend in all?

A $1,365

B $1,355

C $1,255

D $635

6. Miles is 1,196 weeks old. His younger sister Abby is 468 weeks old.

a. Write and solve an equation to show the difference in their ages in weeks.

b. Write and solve an equation to show their total ages.

Name _____

Common Core Georgia Performance Standards Practice

MCC4.NBT.5 Multiply a whole number of up to four digits by a one-digit whole number, and multiply two two-digit numbers, using strategies based on place value and the properties of operations. Illustrate and explain the calculation by using equations, rectangular arrays, and/or area models.

1. Find the product.

$$
\begin{array}{r}
2{,}056 \\
\times9 \\
\hline
\end{array}
$$

2. Find the product.

$$
\begin{array}{r}
89 \\
\times\,27 \\
\hline
\end{array}
$$

3. Hannah is helping her grandmother make a quilt. Each row will have 16 squares. There will be 14 rows.

   a. Draw a model of the quilt.

   b. How many squares will Hannah and her grandmother need to make?

4. Juan bakes and sells dog treats at the farmers market. He always fits 12 treats on a cookie sheet. On Saturday, he bakes 8 batches of dog treats.

   a. Draw an array to match the problem situation.

   b. Write an equation to show how many dog treats Juan bakes.

   c. Solve the equation you wrote.

5. An Olympic-sized swimming pool is 50 meters long and 25 meters wide.

   a. Draw a model to show the area of an Olympic-sized pool.

   b. Write an equation to show the area of an Olympic-sized pool.

   c. Solve the equation you wrote.

6. Principal Watts walks 5 miles every day. How many miles does he walk in 1 year, or 365 days? Write and solve an equation.

Name _____

Common Core Georgia Performance Standards Practice

MCC4.NBT.6 Find whole-number quotients and remainders with up to four-digit dividends and one-digit divisors, using strategies based on place value, the properties of operations, and/or the relationship between multiplication and division. Illustrate and explain the calculation by using equations, rectangular arrays, and/or area models.

1. Find the quotient.

$486 \div 3$

2. Find the quotient.

$1,250 \div 7$

3. Aaron raises chickens. He sells chicken eggs by the dozen. On Friday, Aaron sold 96 eggs. How many dozen eggs did Aaron sell?

a. Draw a rectangular array to model the problem situation.

b. Write an equation that matches the model you drew.

c. Solve the equation you wrote.

4. Claire helps at her mother's flower shop. This week, her mother received a shipment of 250 sunflowers. Claire put them in bundles of 8 flowers. How many bundles did she make? Did she have any bundles with fewer than 8 sunflowers? If so, how many more sunflowers would she need to complete the bundle?

5. A tailor sews 8 buttons on each jacket he makes. He has 220 buttons. On how many jackets can he sew buttons?

6. Green Valley City Park has an area of 6,557 square feet. The length of the park is 83 feet.

   a. Draw a model to show Green Valley City Park.

   b. Write and solve an equation to show how to find the width of the park.

Name _____

Common Core Georgia Performance Standards Practice

MCC4.NF.1 Explain why a fraction $\frac{a}{b}$ is equivalent to a fraction $\frac{(n \times a)}{(n \times b)}$ by using visual fraction models, with attention to how the number and size of the parts differ even though the two fractions themselves are the same size. Use this principle to recognize and generate equivalent fractions.

1. Stella and Brian each heat up a small pizza. Stella cuts her pizza into 4 equal slices. Brian cuts his pizza into 8 equal parts.

   a. Draw models of Stella's pizza and Brian's pizza.

   b. Stella eats two pieces of her pizza. Brian eats four pieces of his pizza. Do they eat the same amount of pizza? Show using models.

2. Which of the fractions below is equivalent to $\frac{1}{3}$? Show why that fraction is equivalent to $\frac{1}{3}$.

   $$\frac{4}{5} \quad \frac{4}{6} \quad \frac{4}{9} \quad \frac{4}{12}$$

3. Which two models show equivalent fractions? Explain how you know.

A   **B**   **C**

4. Four students draw a design for a class flag. Each flag is black and white. Shown below are four designs. Which designs have the same fractions of black and white? Explain how you know.

Madison's design

Kyle's design

Jason's design

Lina's design

Name _____

Common Core Georgia Performance Standards Practice

MCC4.NF.2 Compare two fractions with different numerators and different denominators, e.g., by creating common denominators or numerators, or by comparing to a benchmark fraction such as $\frac{1}{2}$. Recognize that comparisons are valid only when the two fractions refer to the same whole. Record the results of comparisons with symbols >, =, or <, and justify the conclusions, e.g., by using a visual fraction model.

1. Which fraction is less than $\frac{5}{8}$?

   A $\frac{7}{8}$

   B $\frac{6}{8}$

   C $\frac{5}{6}$

   D $\frac{4}{8}$

2. Which fraction is greater than $\frac{1}{7}$?

   A $\frac{1}{5}$

   B $\frac{1}{8}$

   C $\frac{1}{9}$

   D $\frac{1}{10}$

3. A kitchen floor has green, yellow, and white tiles. Of those tiles, $\frac{2}{5}$ are green and $\frac{2}{10}$ are yellow. Are there more green tiles than yellow tiles? Explain how you know.

4. Barry got a small sandwich for lunch and ate $\frac{1}{2}$ of his sandwich. Jonah got a large sandwich and ate $\frac{1}{2}$ of his sandwich. Did Jonah and Barry eat the same amount for lunch?

CC 25

5. Place these fractions on the number line below. Then complete the inequalities.

$\frac{2}{5}$ $\frac{1}{4}$ $\frac{4}{6}$ $\frac{5}{8}$

0          $\frac{1}{2}$ $\frac{2}{2}$

a. $\frac{2}{5}$ _____ $\frac{1}{2}$ and $\frac{4}{6}$ _____ $\frac{1}{2}$ so $\frac{2}{5}$ _____ $\frac{4}{6}$.

b. $\frac{5}{8}$ _____ $\frac{1}{2}$ and $\frac{1}{4}$ _____ $\frac{1}{2}$ so $\frac{5}{8}$ _____ $\frac{1}{4}$.

c. $\frac{4}{6}$ _____ $\frac{1}{2}$ and _____ $\frac{2}{2}$ and $\frac{5}{8}$ _____ $\frac{1}{2}$ and _____ $\frac{2}{2}$ and $\frac{5}{8}$ _____ $\frac{4}{6}$.

6. Tell which fraction is greater: $\frac{6}{8}$ _____ $\frac{6}{10}$. Write < or >.

Draw models of fraction strips to prove your answer.

7. Inez compared the fractions $\frac{1}{5}$ and $\frac{1}{3}$. She said, "I compared the denominators. Because 5 is greater than 3, $\frac{1}{5}$ is greater than $\frac{1}{3}$."

Is Inez correct? Explain your answer.

Name _____

Common Core Georgia Performance Standards Practice

MCC4.NF.3a Understand addition and subtraction of fractions as joining and separating parts referring to the same whole.

1. Nan drew a model to show the addition of two fractions.

   Write an equation to match Nate's model.

   _____ + _____ = _____

2. Amy runs $\frac{2}{5}$ of a mile. Then she walks another $\frac{2}{5}$ of a mile.

   a. How far does Amy run and walk? Use the number line to model the problem.

   b. Write and solve an equation to match your model.

   _____ + _____ = _____

3. Mr. Kopek cuts a pie into 8 equal pieces. He eats two pieces and his son eats three pieces.

   a. What fraction of the pie do Mr. Kopek and his son eat? Draw a model to match the problem.

   b. Write an equation to match your model.

   _____ + _____ = _____

4. Kyle draws a model to show the subtraction of two fractions.

Write an equation to match the model.

_____ − _____ = _____

5. Fen bought $\frac{3}{4}$ yard of cloth. She used $\frac{1}{4}$ yard to make a napkin. How much cloth does she have left?

6. In spring, Toni divided her vegetable garden into 3 equal sections. She planted beans in one section, corn in the second section, and squash in the third section. One day in autumn, Toni harvested all the beans and squash.

a. Draw a model to match the problem situation.

b. What fraction of the garden has Toni not yet harvested?

_____ − _____ = _____

Name _____

Common Core Georgia Performance Standards Practice

MCC4.NF.3b Decompose a fraction into a sum of fractions with the same denominator in more than one way, recording each decomposition by an equation. Justify decompositions, e.g., by using a visual fraction model.

1. Jiro thinks of a fraction. He writes the fraction as a sum.

   $\frac{1}{6} + \frac{1}{6} + \frac{3}{6}$

   What fraction is Jiro thinking of?

2. Chloe uses fractions strips to show $\frac{7}{8}$ as the sum of fractions.

1							
$\frac{1}{8}$	$\frac{1}{8}$	$\frac{1}{8}$	$\frac{1}{8}$	$\frac{1}{8}$	$\frac{1}{8}$	$\frac{1}{8}$	$\frac{1}{8}$

   Draw another way to show $\frac{7}{8}$ as the sum of fractions.

   Write an equation to match your models.

CC 29

3. Write $\frac{7}{8}$ as the sum of unit fractions.

4. Write $1\frac{2}{3}$ as the sum of two fractions that have the same denominator.

Write $1\frac{2}{3}$ as the sum of a whole number and two fractions that have the same denominator.

5. To show a fraction, George placed these fraction strips on his desk.

What fraction does his model show? Write the fraction as a sum of the fractions in the model.

Name _____

Common Core Georgia Performance Standards Practice

MCC4.NF.3c Add and subtract mixed numbers with like denominators, e.g., by replacing each mixed number with an equivalent fraction, and/or by using properties of operations and the relationship between addition and subtraction.

Find the sum or difference. Explain how you found the sum or difference.

1. $3\frac{1}{4} + 2\frac{3}{4} =$

2. $4\frac{5}{6} - 3\frac{1}{6} =$

3. Sherri swam $2\frac{5}{8}$ miles on Monday. She swam $1\frac{1}{8}$ miles on Wednesday.

  a. How many miles did Sherri swim on Monday and Wednesday?

  b. How many more miles did Sherri swim on Monday than on Wednesday? Write an equation and solve.

4. What is the sum of $10\frac{3}{5}$ and $6\frac{3}{5}$?

  A 4

  B $\frac{166}{5}$

  C $16\frac{1}{5}$

  D $17\frac{1}{5}$

5. What addition sentence does the model show?

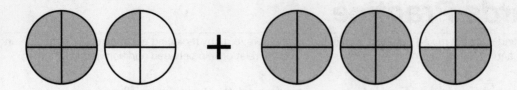

_____ + _____ = _____

6. Subtract. Explain how you found the difference.

$$9\frac{1}{3}$$
$$-1\frac{2}{3}$$

7. Check your answer to problem 6 by adding. Explain how you found your work.

Name _____

Common Core Georgia Performance Standards Practice

MCC4.NF.3d Solve word problems involving addition and subtraction of fractions referring to the same whole and having like denominators, e.g., by using visual fraction models and equations to represent the problem.

1. Georgia is mixing colors to paint a door. She pours $\frac{3}{8}$ cup of red paint into a can. Then she adds $\frac{2}{8}$ cup of blue paint to the can.

   a. How much paint is in the can? Write an equation.

   b. Solve your equation.

2. A piece of tape is $\frac{10}{12}$ inch long. Diego cuts off $\frac{5}{12}$ inch of the piece of tape.

   a. Use the number line to show a model of the problem.

   b. How much tape is left?

3. Erika lives on a farm. Her father uses $\frac{1}{8}$ of the farm land to grow soy beans and $\frac{3}{8}$ of the farm land to grow corn. The rest of the farm land is used grazing land for cattle.

    a. Draw a model to match the problem.

    b. What fraction of the farm land is used to grow crops (corn and soy beans)?

    c. What fraction of the farm land is used for cattle grazing?

4. Jamal spends $\frac{3}{4}$ of an hour writing a short story. Then he spends $\frac{1}{4}$ of an hour revising the story. How much longer does Jamal spend writing than revising? Write and solve an equation.

Name _____

Common Core Georgia Performance Standards Practice

MCC4.NF.4a Understand a fraction $\frac{a}{b}$ as a multiple of $\frac{1}{b}$.

1.

$\frac{1}{4}$	$\frac{1}{4}$	$\frac{1}{4}$	$\frac{1}{4}$

    a. How many sections are shaded? _____

    b. What fraction of the model is shaded? _____

2.

$\frac{1}{5}$	$\frac{1}{5}$	$\frac{1}{5}$	$\frac{1}{5}$	$\frac{1}{5}$

    a. How many sections are shaded? _____

    b. What fraction of the model is shaded? _____

3. Shade parts of the circle to model the fraction $\frac{5}{6}$.

    How many parts did you shade? _____

4. Draw a model to show three equal parts of a whole.
Then shade parts of the model to show $\frac{2}{3}$.

    How many parts did you shade? _____

CC 35

5. Julie divides a board into 8 equal pieces. Draw a model to show Julie's board.

    a. Julie paints $\frac{4}{8}$ of the board.
       How many pieces of the board does she paint? _____

    b. How many pieces of the board are not painted? _____

       What fraction of the board do the unpainted pieces represent? _____

6. Jorge divides a circle into 12 equal slices. Draw a model to match.

    a. Jorge cuts out $\frac{3}{12}$ of the circle.
       How many slices of the circle does he cut out? _____

    b. How many slices of the circle are left? _____

       What fraction of the circle remains? _____

Name _____

Common Core Georgia Performance Standards Practice

MCC4.NF.4b Understand a multiple of $\frac{a}{b}$ as a multiple of $\frac{1}{b}$, and use this understanding to multiply a fraction by a whole number.

1. What is $4 \times \frac{3}{4}$? Explain how you know.

2. What is $2 \times \frac{3}{8}$? Explain how you know.

3. What is $5 \times \frac{2}{3}$? Explain how you know.

4. What is $4 \times \frac{2}{3}$?

8. Find $\frac{5}{6} \times 7$.

5. Multiply $\frac{3}{7}$ and 5.

9. Multiply $\frac{4}{7}$ and 2.

6. What is $3 \times \frac{4}{3}$?

10. What is $5 \times \frac{8}{9}$?

7. Multiply $\frac{3}{5}$ and 6.

11. Multiply $\frac{2}{9}$ and 7.

Name _____

Common Core Georgia Performance Standards Practice

MCC4.NF.4c Solve word problems involving multiplication of a fraction by a whole number, e.g., by using visual fraction models and equations to represent the problem.

1. Fern is helping her mother make decorations for a family gathering. Fern is putting lace around napkins. For each napkin, Fern needs $\frac{3}{5}$ yard of lace. Fern will put the lace on 10 napkins.

   a. Use a number line model to show the problem.

   b. Write an equation to match the model. Use the letter *l* to represent the amount of lace that Fern will need.

   c. How many yards of lace will Fern need? Explain your answer.

2. Mindy wants to paint her room. Her mother tells her that she will need $\frac{2}{3}$ gallon of paint for each of the 4 walls. How much paint will she need?

   a. Draw a model to match the problem.

   b. Write an equation to match the model. Use the letter *p* to represent the amount of paint Mindy will need.

   c. How many gallons of paint will Mindy need to buy? Explain your answer.

3. Vicki has a vegetable garden. She spends $\frac{3}{4}$ hour in her vegetable garden each week end. How many hours will she spend in her garden over the 12 weeks of summer?

a. Use a number line model to show the problem.

b. Write an equation to match the model. Use the letter h to represent the number of hours that Vicki will spend in her garden.

c. How many hours will Vicki spend in the garden? Explain your answer.

4. Frank plays in a soccer league. At each practice, he drinks $\frac{3}{5}$ gallon of sports drink. He practices 5 days a week. How many gallons of sports drink does his mother need to buy each week?

Name _____

Common Core Georgia Performance Standards Practice

MCC4.NF.5 Express a fraction with denominator 10 as an equivalent fraction with denominator 100, and use this technique to add two fractions with respective denominators 10 and 100.

1. For each of these fractions, write the equivalent fraction with a denominator of 100.

   $\dfrac{4}{10} =$ _____ $\dfrac{7}{10} =$ _____

   $\dfrac{2}{10} =$ _____ $\dfrac{9}{10} =$ _____

   $\dfrac{18}{10} =$ _____ $\dfrac{26}{10} =$ _____

2. Find the sums.

   a. $\dfrac{4}{10} + \dfrac{3}{100} =$ _____

   b. $\dfrac{7}{10} + \dfrac{2}{100} =$ _____

   c. $\dfrac{9}{10} + \dfrac{3}{100} =$ _____

   d. $\dfrac{1}{100} + \dfrac{5}{10} =$ _____

   e. $\dfrac{6}{100} + \dfrac{8}{10} =$ _____

Find the sums.

3. $\dfrac{5}{10} + \dfrac{2}{100} = $ _____

4. $\dfrac{7}{100} + \dfrac{2}{10} = $ _____

5. $\dfrac{8}{10} + \dfrac{3}{100} = $ _____

6. $\dfrac{4}{100} + \dfrac{3}{10} = $ _____

7. $\dfrac{6}{100} + \dfrac{1}{10} = $ _____

8. $\dfrac{36}{10} + \dfrac{8}{100} = $ _____

9. $\dfrac{11}{10} + \dfrac{7}{100} = $ _____

10. $\dfrac{5}{100} + \dfrac{2}{10} = $ _____

Name _____

Common Core Georgia Performance Standards Practice

MCC4.NF.6 Use decimal notation for fractions with denominators 10 or 100.

1. Which is the decimal form of $\frac{4}{10}$?

    A 0.4

    B 4.0

    C 0.04

    D 0.44

2. Which fraction equals 0.29?

    A $\frac{2}{9}$

    B $\frac{2}{10}$

    C $\frac{29}{100}$

    D $\frac{29}{10}$

3. Write these fractions in decimal form.

    $\frac{2}{10} =$ _____ $\frac{5}{10} =$ _____

    $\frac{22}{100} =$ _____ $\frac{78}{100} =$ _____

    $\frac{45}{100} =$ _____ $\frac{92}{100} =$ _____

4. Write these decimals as fractions. Use denominators of either 10 or 100.

    0.3 = _____   0.18 = _____

    0.73 = _____   0.8 = _____

    0.48 = _____   0.67 = _____

5. The number line shows tenths from 0 to 1.

0   0.3   1

    a. Write decimals to complete the number line.

    b. Below the number line, add leaders and labels for these three numbers:
        0.68, 0.25, and 0.82.

6. The number line shows tenths from 0 to 1.

0   0.5   1

What decimals are shown by the short lines with letters? If you are not sure,
write your best estimate.

Line A: _____

Line B: _____

Line C: _____

Line D: _____

Why is it difficult to identify lines C and D exactly?

Name _____

Common Core Georgia Performance Standards Practice

MCC4.NF.7 Compare two decimals to hundredths by reasoning about their size. Recognize that comparisons are valid only when the two decimals refer to the same whole. Record the results of comparisons with the symbols >, =, or <, and justify the conclusions, e.g., by using a visual model.

1. Plot these two decimals on the number line below.

   0.43   0.39

   Write an inequality comparing the two decimals. Explain your answer using the number line.

2. Plot these two decimals on the number line below.

   0.28   0.82

   Write an inequality comparing the two decimals. Explain your answer using the number line.

3. The baseball team started the game with two one-liter bottles of water. At the end of the game, the first bottle had 0.3 liters left and the second had 0.4 liters left.

Draw a model to show the amount of water left in each bottle after the game.

Out of which liter bottle did more player take water? the first or the second?

4. Simon and Danielle are on the baseball team. Last season, 0.15 of Simon's hits were home runs, and 0.15 of Danielle's hits were also home runs.

   a. Can you tell whether Simon and Danielle hit the same number of home runs?

   b. Frank is also on the baseball team. Of his hits last season, 0.19 were home runs. Can you tell if he hit more home runs than Simon or Danielle? Explain.

5. Draw a decimal square to represent 0.33 and 0.27.

Which is greater?

_____ < _____

Name _____

Common Core Georgia Performance Standards Practice

MCC4.MD.1 Know relative sizes of measurement units within one system of units including km, m, cm; kg, g; lb, oz.; l, ml; hr, min, sec. Within a single system of measurement, express measurements in a larger unit in terms of a smaller unit. Record measurement equivalents in a two-column table.

1. A distance of 5 kilometers (km) is the same as how many meters (m)?

    A 50 m

    B 500 m

    C 5,000 m

    D 50,000 m

2. A movie lasts 3 hours. How many minutes is this?

    A 30 minutes

    B 60 minutes

    C 120 minutes

    D 180 minutes

3. Change each of these measurements into a smaller unit.

7 kilograms into grams _____

5 pounds into ounces _____

12 meters into centimeters _____

6 hours into minutes _____

9 minutes into seconds _____

2 pound into ounces _____

4 yards into feet _____

4. Decide whether each equation is true or false. If the statement is false, then write the corrected equation on the line to the right.

4 kilometers = 4,000 meters _____

10 pounds = 80 ounces _____

2 minutes = 90 seconds _____

15 liters = 0.15 milliliters _____

3 hours = 180 minutes _____

10 minutes = 300 seconds _____

17 kilograms = 1,700 grams _____

7 meters = 700 centimeters _____

5. Frieda worked on her homework last night for 120 minutes. How many hours did she spend on her homework last night?

6. A scientist measures 5 liters of water in a beaker. How many milliliters of water did the scientist measure in the beaker?

7. How many seconds are in 1 hour? Explain how you know.

Name _____

Common Core Georgia Performance Standards Practice

MCC4.MD.2 Use the four operations to solve word problems involving distances, intervals of time, liquid volumes, masses of objects, and money, including problems involving simple fractions or decimals, and problems that require expressing measurements given in a larger unit in terms of a smaller unit. Represent measurement quantities using diagrams such as number line diagrams that feature a measurement scale.

1. Martha and her family went to the seashore for a week-long vacation. For 5 days of their vacation, they rode bicycles around the area. The table below shows how far they rode each day.

Day	Miles
Monday	5
Tuesday	7
Wednesday	5
Thursday	8
Friday	5

a. How many miles did they ride during their week-long vacation?

b. What was the difference between the longest and the shortest ride?

c. Martha wanted to ride an average of 7 miles a day during the family vacation. To find the average, she took the total number of miles they rode and divided it by the 5 days. What did she find? Did she make her goal?

2. A scientist is carrying out an experiment. She measures 30 milliliters of liquid and pours it into a 100-milliliter beaker. Later, she adds another 25 milliliters of liquid to the beaker. How much more liquid can the scientist add to the beaker?

3. Micah and his father did some laundry at the laundromat. To wash a load costs $2 and to dry a load costs another $2. Micah and his father washed and dried 4 loads of laundry. They also had to buy 4 packets of detergent for $1 per packet.

How much did Micah and his father spend to do their laundry?

4. During the rainy season, the height of a river increases 70 centimeters a day. After how many days will the river increase a total of 3.5 meters?

5. Jeremiah is making a care package for his sister who is away at college. He can send up to 5 pounds for a flat rate of $12.95. He puts some items in the box and then weighs it. And it weighs $2\frac{3}{8}$ pounds. He has more items he would like to send. What else can he add to the box to be as close to 5 pounds without going over? What is the weight of the box with the additional items?

Item	Weight
2 small boxes of dark chocolate truffles	$1\frac{2}{8}$ pound per box
3 packets of candied fruit	$\frac{6}{8}$ pound per packet
2 packet of hair clips	$\frac{1}{8}$ pound per packet
1 small bottle of body lotion	$\frac{5}{8}$ pound per bottle

6. Sam has a piggy bank full of quarters, dimes, nickels, and pennies. Describe two ways he could make $0.78 using only two kinds of coins.

Of the four types of coins, which must Sam use?

7. Naomi stops every 600 meters as she walks a distance of 2.4 kilometers. How many stops does she make?

8. At Hogan Airport, an airplane takes off every 12 minutes. How many airplanes take off in 5 hours?

Name _____

Common Core Georgia Performance Standards Practice

MCC4.MD.3 Apply the area and perimeter formulas for rectangles in real world and mathematical problems.

1. Teresa measures the dimensions of her math book. It is 28 centimeters long and 21 centimeters wide. How can Teresa find the perimeter of her math book?

2. Ted is helping his father plant their vegetable garden this year. They will put a fence around the garden. Ted measures the length of the garden, which is 6 feet. His father tells him that the width is twice the length. How much fencing do Ted and his father need to buy to enclose the garden?

A 36 feet

B 24 feet

C 12 feet

D 6 feet

3. The area of a rectangular bedroom is 240 square feet. If the length of the bedroom is 16 feet, what is the width?

4. As shown below, a room is in the shape of a 9 ft × 5 ft rectangle that has a 3 ft × 4 ft rectangle removed. What is the area of the room? Explain how you found your answer.

5. A rectangular piece of construction paper has length 11 inches and width 8 inches. How could it be cut to make a rectangle of area 32 square inches?

CC 51

6. Tasha is decorating a rectangular bulletin board by putting ribbon around its outer edge. The bulletin board is 14 inches wide and 18 inches tall. How many inches of ribbon does she need?

7. Joey's playhouse has a perimeter of 28 feet. What could be the dimensions of the playhouse? Draw a model and label the length and width. Show that the dimensions equal a perimeter of 28 feet.

8. Janice walked around two sides of a square park. The perimeter of the park is 1,200 yards. How many yards did Janice walk? Explain your answer.

9. Roger just got a new puppy for his birthday. He and his mother will build fence an area in the backyard for the puppy to play in. The play area will be 24 square feet. What dimensions could the play area be? Which dimensions would be the least expensive to fence?

Name _____

Common Core Georgia Performance Standards Practice

MCC4.MD.4 Make a line plot to display a data set of measurements in fractions of a unit ($\frac{1}{2}$, $\frac{1}{4}$, $\frac{1}{8}$). Solve problems involving addition and subtraction of fractions by using information presented in line plots.

1. Ryan's dog just had a litter of 8 puppies. His mother measured the length each of the puppies. The table below shows their lengths in inches.

Puppy	1	2	3	4	5	6	7	8
Length in inches	$8\frac{1}{4}$	$7\frac{3}{4}$	9	$8\frac{3}{4}$	$7\frac{1}{4}$	$7\frac{1}{2}$	$8\frac{1}{4}$	$7\frac{1}{2}$

a. Draw a line plot for the data set.

b. How much shorter is the smallest puppy than the biggest puppy?

c. How many puppies are longer than 8 inches?

d. How many puppies are shorter than 8 inches?

2. Sandy used this table to record how many hours she read each day.

Sandy's Reading Log

Day	Hours Spent Reading
Monday	$\frac{3}{4}$
Tuesday	$\frac{1}{2}$
Wednesday	$1\frac{1}{4}$
Thursday	$1\frac{3}{4}$
Friday	2
Saturday	$1\frac{1}{2}$
Sunday	$3\frac{1}{4}$

a. Make a line plot of the data in the table.

b. How many total hours did Sandy spend reading this week?

c. On which two days did she read more — on Saturday and Sunday or on Wednesday and Thursday? By how much more?

d. What might be some reasons to explain why Sandy read more on those two days?

Name _____

Common Core Georgia Performance Standards Practice

MCC4.MD.5a Recognize angles as geometric shapes that are formed wherever two rays share a common endpoint, and understand concepts of angle measurement: • An angle is measured with reference to a circle with its center at the common endpoint of the rays, by considering the fraction of the circular arc between the points where the two rays intersect the circle. An angle that turns through $\frac{1}{360}$ of a circle is called a "one-degree angle" and can be used to measure angles. **4.MD.5b** Recognize angles as geometric shapes that are formed wherever two rays share a common endpoint, and understand concepts of angle measurement: • An angle that turns through n one-degree angles is said to have an angle measure of n degrees.

1. Look at the angle in the circle.

   a. What fraction of the circle is inside the angle?

   b. A circle has 360°. How can you find the measure of the angle?

   c. What is the measure of the angle?

2. Look at the angle in the circle.

   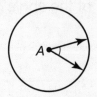

   a. What fraction of the circle is inside the angle?

   b. A circle has 360°. How can you find the measure of the angle?

   c. What is the measure of the angle?

3. Look at the angle in the circle.

   a. What fraction of the circle is inside the angle?

   b. A circle has 360°. How can you find the measure of the angle?

   c. What is the measure of the angle?

4. Look at the angle in the circle.

   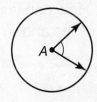

   a. What fraction of the circle is inside the angle?

   b. A circle has 360°. How can you find the measure of the angle?

   c. What is the measure of the angle?

5. Look at the angle in the circle.

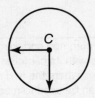

   a. What fraction of the circle
      is inside the angle?

   b. A circle has 360°. How can you
      find the measure of the angle?

   c. What is the measure of
      the angle?

6. Look at the angle in the circle.

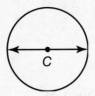

   a. What fraction of the circle
      is inside the angle?

   b. A circle has 360°. How can you
      find the measure of the angle?

   c. What is the measure of
      the angle?

7. Look at the angle in the circle.

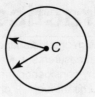

   a. What fraction of the circle
      is inside the angle?

   b. A circle has 360°. How can you
      find the measure of the angle?

   c. What is the measure of
      the angle?

8. Look at the angle in the circle.

   a. What fraction of the circle
      is inside the angle?

   b. A circle has 360°. How can you
      find the measure of the angle?

   c. What is the measure of
      the angle?

Name _____

Common Core Georgia Performance Standards Practice

MCC4.MD.6 Measure angles in whole-number degrees using a protractor. Sketch angles of specified measure.

You will need a protractor for this lesson.

1. Use the protractor to draw an angle at point *O* that measures 75°.

2. Use the protractor to draw an angle at point *O* that measures 140°.

3. Use the protractor to draw an angle at point *O* that measures 90°.

Use the protractor to measure each angle.

7.

5.

8.

6.

9.

Name _____

Common Core Georgia Performance Standards Practice

MCC4.MD.7 Recognize angle measure as additive. When an angle is decomposed into non-overlapping parts, the angle measure of the whole is the sum of the angle measures of the parts. Solve addition and subtraction problems to find unknown angles on a diagram in real world and mathematical problems, e.g., by using an equation with a symbol for the unknown angle measure.

1. Look at the angles below.

a. How can you find the measure of angle *RLM*?

b. Find the measure of angle *RLM* without using a protractor. Explain how you found the measure of the angle.

2. Look at the angles below.

a. How can you find the measure of angle *XYW*?

b. Find the measure of angle *XYW* without using a protractor. Explain how you found the measure of the angle.

...gles form where Lee Street
...ts Elm Street. One angle
...easures 31°. The two angles
add together to make an angle of
180°, which is a straight line.

Lee Street

31°

Elm Street

a. Find the other angle on the
diagram between the two
streets. Label it *a*.

b. What is the measurement of
angle *a*? Write an equation
and solve.

4. Look at the angles below. The
measure of angle *NMS* is twice
the measure of angle *SMB*. Write
an equation to find the measure
of angle *NMS*. Use a letter to
represent the unknown. Then
solve the equation.

N

S

n   22°

M

B

5. In any triangle, the sum of the
measures of the three angles
equals 180°. In one triangle,
the three angles measure 80°,
66°, and *x*. What is *x*? Write an
equation and then solve it.

6. Angle *SRT* and angle *TRU* have
the same measure.

S

150°

Q

72° *x*

x T

R   U

a. How can you find the measure
of angle *SRT*?

b. Write one or more equations
to match your way.

c. What is the measure of angle
SRT?

Name _____

Common Core Georgia Performance Standards Practice

MCC4.G.1 Draw points, lines, line segments, rays, angles (right, acute, obtuse), and perpendicular and parallel lines. Identify these in two-dimensional figures.

1. Draw an acute angle.

Explain why the angle you drew is an acute angle.

2. Circle all of the right angles in the figure shown.

4. Does the figure shown have any perpendicular lines? Label with an X any perpendicular lines.

3. Draw a line and a line segment. Explain how a line is different from a line segment.

5. Draw an obtuse angle.

Explain why the angle you drew is an obtuse angle.

CC 61

... a ray and an angle. Explain
... a ray and an angle are the
...milar, but different.

8. Does the figure shown have any
   pairs of parallel lines? How do you
   know? If there are parallel lines,
   put an X on one pair.

7. Draw two lines that are
   perpendicular. Explain why the
   lines you drew are perpendicular.

9. Does the figure shown have any
   perpendicular lines? How do you
   know? If there are perpendicular
   lines, put an X on one pair.

Name _____

Common Core Georgia Performance Standards Practice

MCC4.G.2 Classify two-dimensional figures based on the presence or absence of parallel or perpendicular lines, or the presence or absence of angles of a specified size. Recognize right triangles as a category, and identify right triangles.

1. Draw these figures in the appropriate column. Some figures may be drawn in two columns.

At least one pair of parallel lines	No pairs of parallel lines	At least one set of perpendicular lines	No perpendicular lines

2. Using the same figures from item 1, draw them in the appropriate column. Some figures may be drawn in two columns.

At least one acute angle	At least one right angle	At least one obtuse angle

...hese figures in the appropriate column. Some figures may be drawn in two columns.

At least one pair of parallel lines	No pairs of parallel lines	At least one set of perpendicular lines	No perpendicular lines

4. Using the same figures from item 1, draw them in the appropriate column. Some figures may be drawn in two columns.

At least one acute angle	At least one right angle	At least one obtuse angle

Name _____

Common Core Georgia Performance Standards Practice

MCC4.G.3 Recognize a line of symmetry for a two-dimensional figure as a line across the figure such that the figure can be folded along the line into matching parts. Identify line-symmetric figures and draw lines of symmetry.

1. Draw one or more lines of symmetry through the figure below.

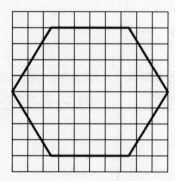

2. Draw one or more lines of symmetry through the figure below.

3. Draw one or more lines of symmetry through the figure below.

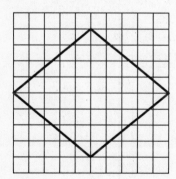

4. Draw one or more lines of symmetry through the figure below.

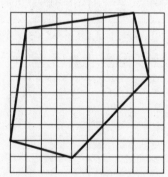

5. Determine the number of lines symmetry for each shape. Draw the shapes in the correct boxes. Some boxes may have more than one shape. Some boxes may have no shapes.

No lines of symmetry	Exactly one line of symmetry	Exactly two lines of symmetry	More than two lines of symmetry

Name _____

Practice End-of-Year Assessment

1. Use the protractor to draw an angle of 40°.
One side of the angle is drawn for you.

2. Circle all of the fractions that are greater than $\frac{4}{9}$.

$\frac{4}{5}$ $\frac{4}{10}$ $\frac{4}{8}$ $\frac{4}{12}$ $\frac{4}{20}$ $\frac{4}{6}$ $\frac{4}{11}$ $\frac{4}{7}$

3. The table shows three bills that the Brock family paid in March. Find the total of the three bills.

Hockey gear	$862
Car repair	$1,055
New carpeting	$3,293

4. Tell whether the equation below is true. Shade the model to explain your answer $\frac{7}{10} \overset{?}{=} \frac{70}{100}$.

5. At 3:00 P.M., Ted and Bonnie both leave Hale School on their bicycles. Ted rides west $3\frac{1}{3}$ miles to his house. Bonnie rides east $3\frac{2}{3}$ miles to her house. How far do Ted and Bonnie live from each other?

6. At the school book fair, 4 times as many volunteers worked on Wednesday as on Monday. There were 16 volunteers on Wednesday.

Write an equation that you can use to find how many volunteers worked at the book fair on Monday. Use the letter M to represent the number of Monday volunteers.

7. Rectangle *ABCD* is shown below, along with the diagonal $\overline{AC}$. Which two line segments are perpendicular to each other?

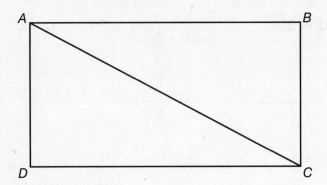

A $\overline{AC}$ and $\overline{AB}$

B $\overline{AB}$ and $\overline{DC}$

C $\overline{AD}$ and $\overline{AC}$

D $\overline{AD}$ and $\overline{DC}$

8. A marble factory produces 3,250 marbles a day. The marbles are gathered in groups of 8 and placed in a bag. How many bag of marbles does the factory produce each day? Explain how you found your answer.

9. Write an inequality comparing 45.82 and 45.79. Use the appropriate math symbol. Tell how you know which number is greater.

10. Hank's family orders three large pizzas for dinner every Friday night. Each pizza is cut into 8 equal slices. Last Friday, Hand ate two pizzas from each of the three pizzas.

  a. Draw a model to show what Hank ate.

  b. Write an equation that matches your model.

  c. Did Hank eat more or less than one full pizza? Explain how you know.

11. Jake goes with his mother to the animal shelter one afternoon each week. Last week, he counted the number of cats and dogs at the shelter. He counted 7 cats and 3 times as many dogs as cats.

  a. Write an equation that can be used to find the number of dogs that Jake counted. Use the letter d to represent the number of dogs.

  b. How many dogs did Jake count at the shelter?

12. Find the difference. 540.7 − 932.4.

13. Find a fraction that is equal to $\frac{4}{12}$. Draw models to prove that the two fraction are equivalent.

14. Write $\frac{4}{10}$ as a decimal.

15. What is 23,702 rounded to the nearest thousand? Explain your answer.

16. Triangle *ABC* is an equilateral triangle. Each angle measures 60°. What is the measure of angle *x*?

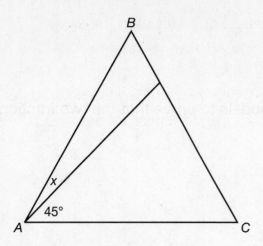

17. Find the difference.

$$7\frac{1}{4} - 3\frac{3}{4}$$

18. Hannah helps her grandfather harvest corn at his farm. She measures the length of 10 ears of corn and record the lengths in a table.

Ear of corn	1	2	3	4	5	6	7	8	9	10
Length in inches	$13\frac{1}{2}$	$14\frac{1}{4}$	$13\frac{3}{4}$	$14\frac{1}{2}$	$14\frac{1}{4}$	14	$15\frac{1}{4}$	$14\frac{1}{2}$	$14\frac{3}{4}$	$14\frac{3}{4}$

a. Make a line plot to show the lengths of the ears of corn.

b. How much longer is the longest ear of corn compared to the shortest?

c. How many ears of corn are longer than 14 inches?

19. Which of these statements about the number below is true?

233,232

A The first 2 represents a value that is 10 times greater than the second 2.

B The first 3 represents a value that is one hundred times greater than the second 3.

C The first 3 represents a value that is 10 times greater than the second 3.

D The first 2 represents a value that is one hundred times greater than the second 2.

20. Find the quotient.

2,444 ÷ 7.

21. List all of the factor pairs for the number 42.

22. Mitchell School held a food drive. Students brought in canned goods for one week. At the end of the week, all of the canned goods were brought to a food pantry. The table shows how many canned goods the students in three grades brought in.

Grade	Number of Canned Goods
Grade 3	106
Grade 4	251
Grade 5	263

How many canned goods did the students in these three grades bring in? Write an equation and solve it.

23. Today, Leela is 10 years older than her sister Amy. Her age is also 3 times Amy's age.

a. Write an equation to compare Leela's age and Amy's age. Use the letter L to represent Leela's age and the letter A to represent Amy's age.

b. Write another equation that uses a different operation to compare Leela's age and Amy's age. Use the letter L to represent Leela's age and the letter A to represent Amy's age.

c. As Leela and Amy get older, which of the two equations will always be true? Explain why.

24. Write a number statement to compare the numbers 1,217 and 1,388. Explain how you know which number is greater.

25. Figure *ABCD* is a rectangle, and Point *X* is on the side of the rectangle between points *A* and *B*. A line segment connects point *X* and point *C*.

How many right angles does figure *AXCD* have?

A 0

B 1

C 2

D 4

26. Find the product of 2,386 and 4.

27. Place these fractions on the number line below.

$$\frac{5}{8}, \frac{1}{8}, \frac{7}{8}, \frac{3}{8}$$

a. Compare $\frac{3}{8}$ and $\frac{1}{8}$ by comparing them to a benchmark fraction on the number line.

b. Compare $\frac{5}{8}$ and $\frac{7}{8}$ by comparing them to a benchmark fraction on the number line.

28. Gigi says that 4,271 rounded to the nearest hundred is 4,200.

    a. Is her answer correct? Explain how you know.

    b. What should be the answer?

29. Libby and Josh bake a pie with Libby's grandmother. Libby wants to take home $\frac{1}{6}$ of the pie, while Josh wants to take home $\frac{3}{6}$ of it. How much pie will Libby's grandmother have?

    a. Draw a model to match the problem situation.

    b. Write an equation to match the model you drew.

    c. Solve the equation you wrote. How much pie will Libby's grandmother have?

CC 77

30. Rina's town has voted to build a new park. The park will be 25 feet long and 15 feet wide.

a. Draw a model of the park.

b. What will be the area of the park?

31. Draw models to compare these fractions: $\frac{3}{5}$, $\frac{3}{4}$, and $\frac{1}{2}$.

32. Use models to compare these two decimals. Which is greater?

0.7   0.07

33. Brian gets a weekly allowance of $10. He decides to save $3 each week from his allowance. Complete the table below to show how much he will save in 6 weeks.

Week	1	2	3	4	5	6
Savings	$3.00					

34. One morning, Sue milked 8 dairy goats. Each goat produced $\frac{3}{4}$ liter of milk. How much milk did Sue get from the 8 goats?

   a. Write an equation to find how much milk Sue got from the goats. Use the letter T to represent the amount of milk.

   b. Solve the equation to find T in liters.

35. Find the product.

     $5{,}087 \times 5?$

36. Stan and Kayli are painting a fence. Stan paints $\frac{1}{8}$ of the fence and Kayli paints $\frac{3}{8}$ of the fence. How much of the fence do they paint together?

37. A large carton of fresh produce has a mass of 32 kilograms. What is mass in grams?

38. Find the sum.

$$\frac{7}{10} + \frac{3}{100}?$$

39. The staff at Trudy's Cafe sold 104 cups of coffee on Saturday, which was 4 times as many cups as they sold on Sunday.

a. Write an equation that can be used to determine how many cups of coffee Trudy's Cafe sold on Sunday.

b. Solve the equation to find the number of cups sold on Sunday.

40. Write the expanded form of 3,062.

41. Draw lines to match the fraction with the decimal.

0.37 $\frac{3}{10}$

0.54 $\frac{54}{100}$

0.5 $\frac{5}{10}$

0.3 $\frac{37}{100}$

42. Leah wrote a 5-digit number on a piece of paper. She gave her friend Karen these clues to find the number.

What number did Leah write?

a. The 3 is in the place that is ten times greater than the place where the 5 is.

b. The 5 is in the place that is one hundred times less than the place where the 8 is.

c. The 2 is in the place that is ten times less than the place where the 5 is.

d. The 9 is in the place that is ten times greater than the place where the 8 is.

43. Draw a line of symmetry on this image.

44. Joni's mother is an event planner, She is planning a dinner for 432 guests. The banquet room has small round tables that seat 6 guests and large round tables that seat 10 guests.

a. How many tables will Joni's mother need if she uses the small tables? Write an equation to find the number of small tables. Use the letter *s* to represent the small tables. Then find the solution.

b. How many tables will Joni's mother need if she uses the large tables? Write an equation to find the number of large tables. Use the letter *l* to represent the large tables.

45. Draw models to show that $\frac{2}{3} = \frac{4}{6}$.

Name _____

Practice Performance Task 1

Camp Walkie-Talkies

Mathematical Content Focus:	Mathematical Practice Focus:
4.OA.3, 4.NBT.5, 4.NBT.6, 4.MD.2	1, 2, 3, and 6

Part A

The treasurer of a camp has a $1,000 budget to buy walkie-talkies for 56 campers. Each camper must have a walkie-talkie. The camp treasurer has narrowed down the choices to two models, Model A and Model B.

Each model has different prices depending on how they are ordered. The prices, including tax, for Model A and Model B are shown below.

Walkie-Talkie Model A

Box with 6 pair—$34/pair
1 pair—$42/pair

Walkie-Talkie Model B

Box with 24 pair—$33/pair
1 pair—$53/pair

1. Which model can the camp treasurer order with his $1,000 budget? Show and explain your work. Use a model to explain your calculations.

...ctor of the same camp wants to make sure that when the older campers ...i their 6-day hike, they will be able to use the new walkie-talkies during ...ch day of the hike. She learns that both models have 15 hours of talk time (the amount of time a person can talk without recharging batteries). She will direct the camp counselors to set a limit on the number of minutes the campers can use the walkie-talkies each day of the hike.

2. How long can each camper use his or her walkie-talkie each day if it is used for the same amount of time each day?

3. Write an equation to show how you solved the problem in Question 2.
Let t = the amount of time a camper can use the walkie-talkie each day.

Name _____

Practice Performance Task 2
Animal Shelter Volunteers

Mathematical Content Focus:	Mathematical Practice Focus:
4.NF.2, 4.NF.3, 4.NF.4	1, 2, 4, 7, and 8

Part A

Roshanna and LeShan volunteer at their local animal shelter on Wednesdays after school. At the shelter they feed the dogs their afternoon meal according to the amounts of food given in the table below.

Other volunteers feed the dogs the same amounts in the morning. Each dog eats the same brand and type of food as the other dogs.

1. How much dog food does the shelter use each day to feed Tessa and Bubba? Use an equation and pictures of fraction models to support your answer.

Dog	Amount of Dog Food per meal
Dante	$\frac{2}{3}$ cup
Shaggy	$\frac{1}{2}$ cup
Tessa	$\frac{3}{4}$ cup
Milo	$\frac{2}{3}$ cup
Sasha	$\frac{1}{2}$ cup
Bubba	$\frac{3}{4}$ cup

2. How much dog food does the shelter use each week to feed Dante and Milo?

Part B

Alia also volunteers at the same shelter. She feeds the cats in the shelter. The table shows the amount of food she gives to each cat each day.

Cat	Amount of Cat Food
Rascal	$\frac{5}{8}$ cup
Baggie	$\frac{1}{2}$ cup
Tabitha	$\frac{3}{4}$ cup
Tiger	$\frac{2}{3}$ cup

3. Compare the amount of food Rascal eats in a day with the amount of food Baggie eats in a day. Give two different comparisons. Show visual models to support your comparisons. Use the > sign in one comparison and the < sign in the other comparison.

4. Alia feeds the cats in order of the amount of cat food that they are fed. She starts with the cat who gets the least amount of food. In what order does Alia feed all of the cats?